CONTENTS

Contributors:
Charley Darbishire
Simon Little
Andy Park
Glenn Rogers
Claire Thompson
Chrissy Williams

Consultant:
Maf Gibbons

Published by Coordination Group Publications Ltd
ISBN 1 84146 457 0
Groovy website: www.cgpbooks.co.uk

Printed by Elanders Hindson, Newcastle upon Tyne.
Clipart sources: CorelDRAW and VECTOR.
With thanks to Microsoft, Logotron, KITE and Data Harvest
for permission to use screenshots from MS Word and MS Excel;
Junior ViewPoint; Flowol; and Sensing Science respectively.

Collages

You've probably made collages before in art lessons. They're quite fun.

Make a Collage by Sticking Things on a Backing

The backing could be something like a piece of card, and you can stick anything you like onto it. I made this collage about the countryside.

An old photo of my favourite cow.

A picture of a cat I drew at school.

Some plants I was given by my cousin, Eddie.

A picture from a magazine.

A drawing I did when I was young.

My favourite cartoon character — Felix the Rooster.

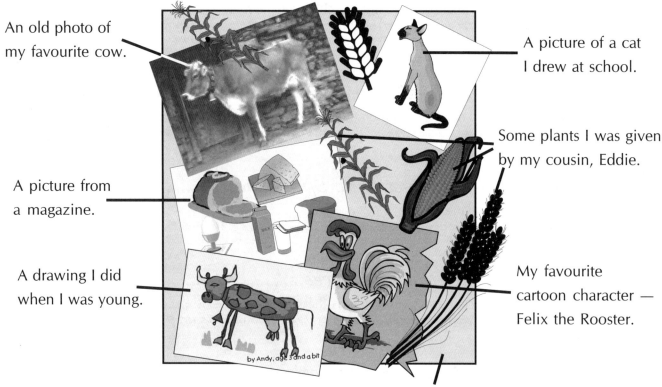

The backing's a piece of cardboard.

You Can Move Bits of Collage Around *(if you don't stick them down)*

One of the things about collages is that you can move all the separate bits about. So if you don't like your collage as it is, you can make a new one — kind of.

 I rearranged all the different bits of my collage.

 I removed the picture of a cat.

 I added a picture of a tractor instead.

Some computer programs work a bit like a collage.

<u>Collages</u>

① <u>How do you make a collage?</u>

....

....

② <u>Which of these pieces of art is a collage?</u>

Tick the box next to the collage.

The Mona Lisa,
by Leonardo da Vinci

Statue of Rolf Harris,
by Leonardo di Caprio

Famous People and their
Favourite Vegetables,
by Leonardo de Ninja

③ <u>What's the difference between a collage and a painting?</u>

Draw a (sausage) around the correct answer.

You can move bits
of a collage around.

They're exactly
the same.

You can move parts
of a painting around.

④ <u>Which is a collage and which is a cottage?</u>

One of these pictures shows a collage, while the other shows a cottage.
Label the pictures correctly.

....

....

Painting Software

You've used things like Microsoft Paint before — it's a type of 'painting software'.

Painting Software Doesn't Work Like a Collage

Microsoft Paint doesn't work like a collage. It's like doing a real painting. Look at this...

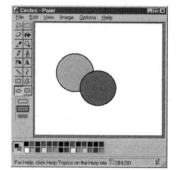

1. This is a design made up of 2 circles.

2. The dark-grey circle covers part of the light-grey circle. This bit of the light-grey circle is lost forever.

3. I can't move the circles like pieces of a collage.

4. So I can't get the light-grey circle back by moving the dark-grey one.

You Can Only Move Part of a Picture Using Paint

You can use 'Cut' and 'Paste' to move part of a picture in Paint.
But this isn't like moving part of a collage.

 You can select and move this square chunk of the painting...

 ...or you can carefully select and move just the dark-grey circle.

But whatever I do, I leave a big 'hole' in the light-grey circle.

Painting Software Isn't Great for Drawing Maps

You could make a 'map' of your classroom showing all the desks and chairs, and then 'try out' different arrangements of furniture. This would show you how it would look without having to move all the real furniture.

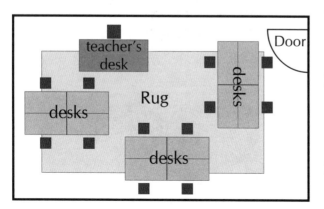

1. This is a plan of a classroom — I made it using painting software.

2. It would be nice to make more space in the middle of the classroom by moving the desks next to the wall.

3. But if I move a desk in this picture, I'll leave a big 'hole' in the rug underneath.

Painting Software

① Fill in the gaps using the words in the wibbly box.

> painting software   collages   real painting   the circle

Microsoft Paint is an example of .... Painting software

isn't very good for making .... That's because using painting software is a

bit like doing a .... So if I paint a square, and then paint a

circle on top, I can't move ....

and get my square back.

② Which of these could a painting program do?

Look at these pictures and tick the changes that could be made using a painting program.

a) ....

b) ....

c) ....

d) ....

> Now see if you're right by trying to make these changes using Microsoft Paint.

③ What will happen if I move the window?

I made this picture using a painting program, but I put the light-grey window in the wrong place. What will happen if I try and move the window? Tick the right answer.

☐ I'll have to move all the other windows too.

☐ I'll leave a big 'hole' in the wall.

☐ The window will turn dark grey.

☐ The door will fall off.

Drawing Software

Painting software is good for some things. But for others, a drawing program is better.

You Can Use 'Word' as a Drawing Program

Microsoft Word is a word processor. But you can use it as a drawing program too.

☼ It's best to have the 'Drawing Toolbar' on screen when you're making pictures.

☼ Turn this on using the View menu.

Drawing Programs are Object-Based

It's easy to draw lines and other shapes on the screen. Any line or shape that you put on the screen is called an object. Drawing programs are often called object-based programs.

Just click here for a line...

...here for a square or rectangle.

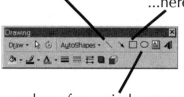

...or here for a circle or an oval.

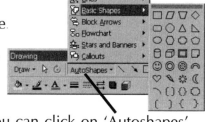

Or you can click on 'Autoshapes' and get loads more fancy shapes.

Just Click and Drag

Drawing programs are usually pretty easy to use.

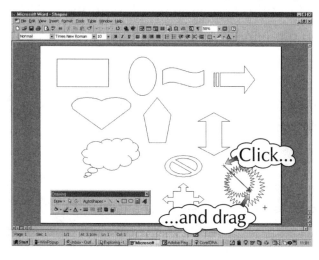

☼1☼ Select the kind of shape you want on the toolbar...

☼2☼ ...click on the page and hold down the mouse button...

☼3☼ ...then just drag out a shape.

Try this:

See what happens if you hold down 'Ctrl' or 'Shift' while you're dragging a shape.

Drawing Software

① You don't have to use painting software for pictures.

There's a different kind of software you can use to make pictures.
What is it called? Draw a picture frame around the correct answer.

Database   Spreadsheet   Internet

Drawing program   Tomb Raider

② What's another name for this kind of program?

....

③ How do you make a shape in a drawing program?

Put these steps in the right order to make a shape on screen.

> a. Click somewhere on the screen, and hold the mouse button down.
> b. Click a shape on the toolbar.
> c. Drag the mouse, still holding down the mouse button.

Correct order: 1) ....   2) ....   3) ....

④ Match these shapes to their buttons on the toolbars.

Draw a circle round each shape's button, and a line from your circle to the shape it makes.

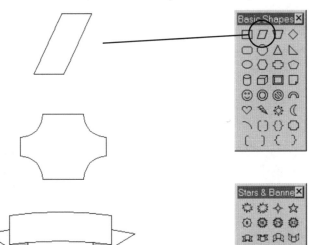
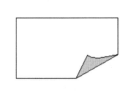

Changing Shapes

Once you've made a shape, you can change how it looks. This is the biggest difference between drawing and painting programs — the way you can change objects so easily.

Select the object you want to change

You have to select an object before you can change anything about it.
An object could be a line or a shape. You select an object by clicking on it.

 When you select a shape these white handles appear. Drag them to change the size of the shape.

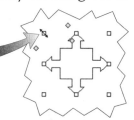

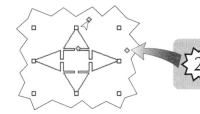

With some shapes in Word, yellow handles appear as well. Moving these changes the shape in different ways.

 You can rearrange shapes on the page dead easily. To move a shape — just select it and drag it.

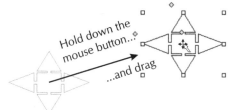

Hold down the mouse button... ...and drag

Change the Colours of the 'Outline' and 'Fill'

Changing the colour of a shape's outline or fill is as easy as pressing a button or two.

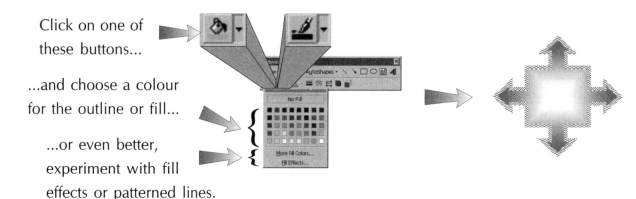

Click on one of these buttons...

...and choose a colour for the outline or fill...

...or even better, experiment with fill effects or patterned lines.

...and more besides

But even cooler than that — if you're using Microsoft Word, you can:

(i)   add arrow heads to lines,

(ii) make your shape 3D,

(iii) add a shadow...

Play about, and see what you can do.

Changing Shapes

1a) What must you do before you can change an object?

....

1b) What happens when you do this?

....

2) Which handle do I need to use?

Which handles could I drag to make this picture:

a. wider, but not taller   ....   or   ....

b. taller, but not wider   ....   or   ....

(There are 2 answers for each.)

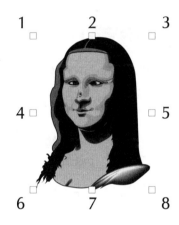

3) You can change an object's colour.

There are two 'parts' of an object you can change the colour of. What are they?

.... and   ....

4) Which button do you need to use?

Write 'outline' and 'fill' next to the correct button.

   ....

   ....

Layers

With object-based programs, you can put objects behind or in front of other objects.

Object-Based Programs Use 'Layers'

This is a really big difference between using an object-based drawing package and a painting package. You definitely can't do this in a painting program.

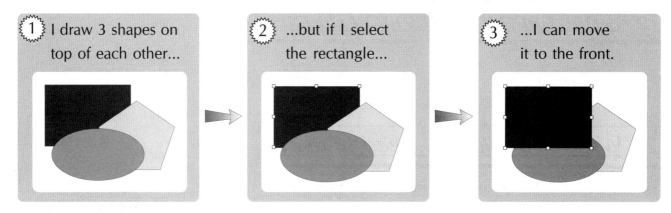

1. I draw 3 shapes on top of each other...
2. ...but if I select the rectangle...
3. ...I can move it to the front.

- This is because objects are put on the screen in 'layers'.
  - Drawing a new shape on top of another doesn't destroy anything.
    - It's more like putting pieces of paper down on a table — you can always get the piece of paper from the bottom of the pile and put it on the top.
      - This kind of software is much more like making a collage.

In Microsoft Word, you move an object from one layer to another by clicking on 'Draw', then 'Order'.

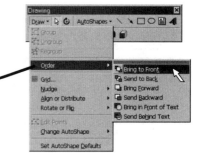

You Can Copy and Paste Objects

You can use 'Copy' and 'Paste' to create copies of objects. It works in the same way for objects in a drawing program as it does for text in a word processor.

'Copy' one raindrop...

...and keep 'Pasting' until your screen looks like the Lake District.

<u>*Layers*</u>

(1) <u>*Only one of these sentences is true.*</u>

Tick the sentence that's true. You may think another one is true as well, but it isn't.

☐ Object-based programs use layers.

☐ Painting programs use layers.

☐ Both object-based and painting programs use layers.

(2) <u>*I draw these three shapes in an object-based program.*</u>

Which picture on the right shows what would happen if I moved the triangle?
Tick the correct diagram.

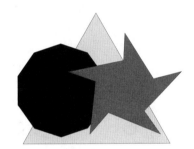

 ☐

 ☐

(3) <u>*Match the buttons to what they do.*</u>

Draw long wiggly peppermint toothpaste worms to show what these buttons do.

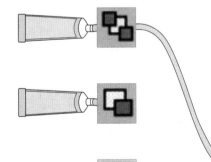
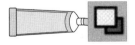

Move the selected object down one layer.

Move the selected object up one layer.

Move the selected object to the bottom layer.

Move the selected object to the top layer.

Making Pictures Using Objects

You can do so much with drawing programs. They're great.

Draw Any Shape You Like

A good drawing program lets you do all sorts of things.

As well as using shapes like squares and circles, you can draw...

① ...curves...

② ...other shapes...

③ ...or 'freehand'.

This means you can draw any shape you like with a bit of practice. And you can 'fill' your shapes too, if the end of your line is in the same place as the beginning.

You Can Rotate Shapes and Lines

You can rotate any shapes you draw.

In Microsoft Word you click on this button...

...and drag the little green handles.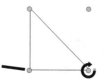

Combine Objects into Complicated Pictures

You can combine lots of different objects to make quite complicated pictures.

 This is supposed to be a cat.
It's made up of different shapes and lines.

 With object-based programs, you can change the individual shapes.

I changed the eyes, ears and eyebrows to change the expression on the cat's face.

Changing a few triangles can change everything...

This is why object-based drawing programs are so great — you can change lots of things about your picture by playing with a few squares and triangles.

Making Pictures Using Objects

① Fill in the gap.

As well as letting you draw circles and squares, a drawing program will let you draw curves, other shapes or ....

② What do I get if I rotate this shape?

Which 2 shapes do I get if I rotate the shape on the left? Tick the correct boxes.

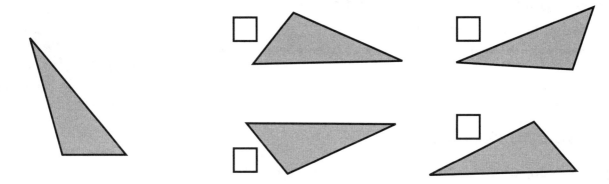

③ Draw your favourite farmyard animal.

But you can only use circles, rectangles, triangles and simple lines.

Don't make it too complicated, because you have to draw it on a computer afterwards.

I've already drawn you a barn — just to put you in the right mood.

 **Computer Activity** ## Make a Masterpiece

You'll need an object-based drawing program for these two projects.

In this project you will:

Make a work of art

- ✓ This is a painting by a famous painter called Matisse. It's called 'The Snail'.
- ✓ It's made out of lots of different coloured shapes.
- ✓ You're going to use an object-based drawing program to create something similar.

Create your work of art

 Use your drawing program to create some different shapes.

 Make them different sizes and colours, and rotate some of your shapes.

 Arrange your shapes into a bit of a mess — like Matisse did.

 Experiment with different arrangements until you like your creation.
You could try: (i)   moving or rotating shapes
(ii) making them different sizes
(iii) moving the shapes into different layers

Don't forget to give your work of art a name

🟊 This is a picture I made.

🟊 I've called it 'The Zebra'.

🟊 It doesn't look much like a zebra.

🟊 But it doesn't matter.
Matisse's picture doesn't look much like a snail.

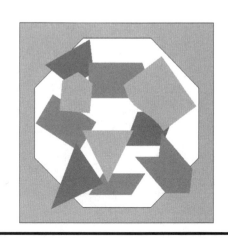

Find a Criminal

In this project you will:

Make a 'Wanted Poster'

This project's a bit tougher.

You have to make a 'Wanted Poster' for someone who recently committed a crime.

> ✓ First of all you need to think of a crime that's been committed.
> ✓ Then you need to draw the criminal's face.
> ✓ You'll also need to show what the criminal might look like in disguise.

Decide on the crime

You need to decide what crime has been committed.

- It could be throwing a custard pie at a teacher.
- Or maybe impersonating a melon in class.

Draw the criminal

This is the fun bit.

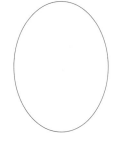
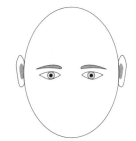

1. Draw an egg shape for the head.

2. Add some eyes and ears in the middle.

3. Then add the hair.

4. And finally the other features.

Show some possible disguises

You could also show some possible disguises on your poster.

✴ You could change your criminal's haircut.

✴ Or you could add something like an eyepatch or a hat.

Wanted
Simon Tiny

For impersonating a
mushroom

Possible disguises

These pictures were mainly made using 'curves' and 'other shapes'. See the top of page 12 for a bit more info.

Modelling

Modelling means showing something real in a different way. A map is a type of model.

Model Your Classroom with Drawing Software

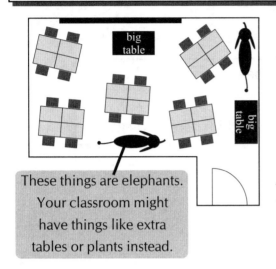

These things are elephants. Your classroom might have things like extra tables or plants instead.

1. This is a model of a classroom for 20 students.

2. It's drawn to a scale of 1 centimetre to 1 metre.

3. This means that 1 centimetre on the model shows 1 metre of the real classroom.

I can move all these shapes around on screen. This means I could see what different arrangements of desks might look like, without moving all the furniture in the classroom.

Models Can Help You Answer Questions

Two extra students are joining the class, so the teacher needs more desks and chairs. She can try out different arrangements of furniture using the model.

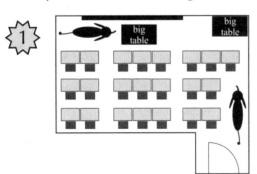 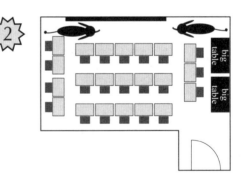

Both of these are very crowded. The teacher wants to try something different.

Try Out Expensive Alternatives... For Free

Someone suggests getting different-sized desks that 4 students can sit around. Also, the teacher decides to get rid of one of the big tables and both of the elephants.

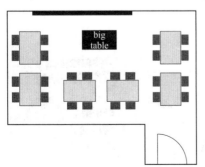

1. This seems to work much better.

2. It means buying new tables.

3. But at least the teacher knows it will be worth it.

Modelling

① What is a model?

....

② Why is it sometimes a good idea to use a model?

Draw (sausages) around the correct answers.

It can be an easier way to try an idea out.

Models can cook dinner for you.

It can be a cheaper way to try an idea out.

③ Use this model to work out how much I can carry.

This is a scale drawing of a tray in a restaurant, along with 2 bowls of chips. The large bowl of chips has enough chips for 2 people, while the small one has enough for 1 person.

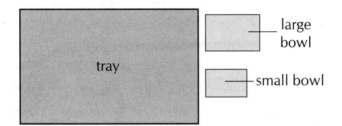

tray

large bowl

small bowl

Work out how many people I can carry chips for.

....

You could cut out 10 pieces of paper the same size as each bowl of chips and try fitting them onto the drawing.

④ Where can I put the new emus in my zoo?

Here is a scale model of my zoo.

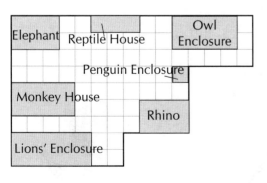

Elephant Reptile House Owl Enclosure

Penguin Enclosure

Monkey House

Rhino

Lions' Enclosure

A big new enclosure like this is going to be built for some emus.

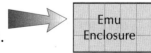

Emu Enclosure

Complete this empty zoo plan to show how I could fit the new emu enclosure into my zoo.

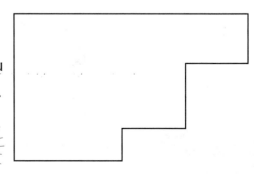

You might need to move some of the other enclosures.

Computer Activity

Modelling Project

You'll need a drawing package for this project.

In this project you will:

Plan improvements to the school grounds

If your school's grounds are very big, just use the part you'd like to improve most.

Draw a map to show how the site looks now:

You need to make a map of the grounds to show what they look like now.

1 Sketch a map of some important things in the school grounds.

2 To draw your map to scale, you could count how many steps it takes you to walk between each thing. Then you'll need to measure how long one of your steps is.
If 1 step = 60 centimetres, then 40 steps = 40 × 60 cm = 2400 cm = 24 metres.

3 You might end up with a sketch map like this.

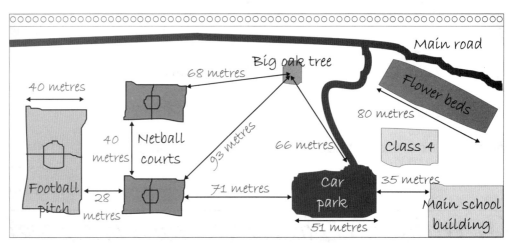

Enter your map onto a computer using an object-based program:

Now you need to build your sketch map on the computer.

You can make a pretty good map using just rectangles, circles and lines.

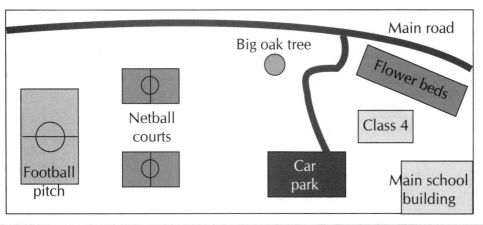

Modelling Project

Think of things that would improve the site:

Make a list of all the things that you think should be changed.

* Maybe you think your school should have some swings.
  Or perhaps a nice rollercoaster.

* You could suggest a nature conservation area, where you could
  go to see animals and flowers growing.

* A giant chessboard painted on the ground might be a nice idea.

* Or you could suggest that the football pitch is turned into an ice rink.

It could be anything — you decide what you want. But be ready to say why you want it.

Show these things on your map:

Now you can show all your suggestions on your map.

Show all the changes you want to make. Like these:

1. More oak trees planted

2. A giant chessboard

3. A nature area

4. A new café

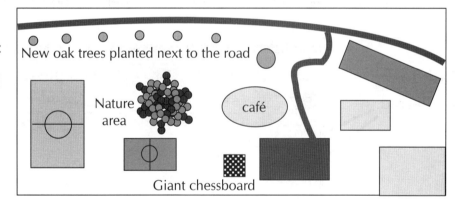

New oak trees planted next to the road

Nature area

café

Giant chessboard

But make sure you don't disturb anything important:

There are a couple of important things you have to remember.

> ✓ You can't disturb anything important like buildings and roads.
>
> ✓ Draw things roughly the right size. For example, rollercoasters
>   need a lot of space — you have to show this on your map.

How will the school look with your improvements?

You could even try sketching what the school will look like after your improvements have been made. Show your teachers how great everything will look.

Databases

Databases contain information

I'm using a database with information about planets and moons in our solar system.

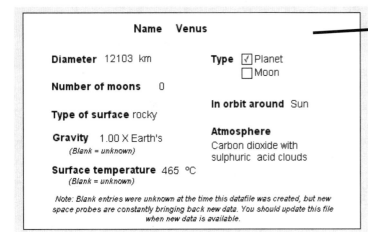

Each planet or moon has a **"record"** of information like this.

Each record is organised into **"fields"** of information.

This database has many fields including name, diameter, type, number of moons and surface temperature.

I can look at all the records of a database together by choosing list or table view.

Each row is a record.

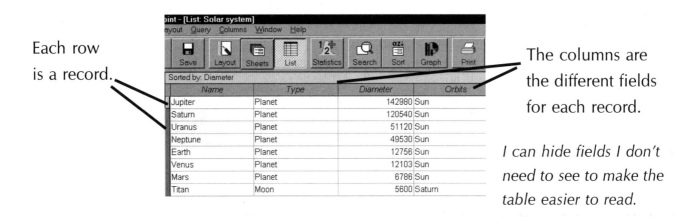

The columns are the different fields for each record.

I can hide fields I don't need to see to make the table easier to read.

It's dead easy to sort databases

Dead easy. I can put the planet names into alphabetical order.
Or I could sort the planets into order of size — whatever I feel like really.

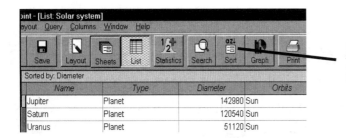

Just press the sort button, and choose the field to sort.

Databases

① Which of these are true statements about databases?

Tick the correct statements about databases.

Databases store <u>used tissues</u>. ☐   Databases store <u>information</u>. ☐

Information about each <u>thing</u> is stored in a <u>record</u>. ☐

Information about each <u>thing</u> is stored in a <u>fish tank</u>. ☐

Each <u>Des O'Connor</u> record is broken down into very <u>small pieces</u>. ☐

Each record is broken down into separate <u>fields</u> of information. ☐

② What type of information do these fields store?

Say whether each field below stores **text**, a **number** or a **choice**.

Different fields store different types of information.
Some fields store numbers, some store text, and some have choices.

Diameter .... *number* ....

Number of moons ....

Type ....

Type of Surface ....

Atmosphere ....

Surface Temperature ....

> **Name** Neptune
>
> **Diameter** 49530 km   **Type** ☑ Planet
>   ☐ Moon
>
> **Number of moons**   8
>   **In orbit around** Sun
> **Type of surface** gassy
>
> **Gravity** 1.10 X Earth's   **Atmosphere**
>   *(Blank = unknown)*   Hydrogen Helium Methane
>
> **Surface temperature** -214 °C
>   *(Blank = unknown)*
>
> *Note: Blank entries were unknown at the time this datafile was created, but new space probes are constantly bringing back new data. You should update this file when new data is available.*

③ Use "field" or "record" to complete these sentences.

This screenshot shows the planets database in **list view**.

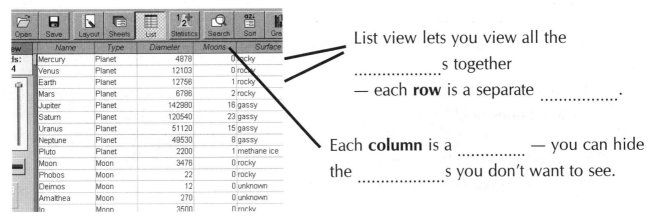

Name	Type	Diameter	Moons	Surface
Mercury	Planet	4878	0	rocky
Venus	Planet	12103	0	rocky
Earth	Planet	12756	1	rocky
Mars	Planet	6786	2	rocky
Jupiter	Planet	142980	16	gassy
Saturn	Planet	120540	23	gassy
Uranus	Planet	51120	15	gassy
Neptune	Planet	49530	8	gassy
Pluto	Planet	2200	1	methane ice
Moon	Moon	3476	0	rocky
Phobos	Moon	22	0	rocky
Deimos	Moon	12	0	unknown
Amalthea	Moon	270	0	unknown
Io	Moon	3500	0	rocky

List view lets you view all the
................s together
— each **row** is a separate ....

Each **column** is a .... — you can hide
the ....s you don't want to see.

Doing Database searches

You can search Databases

 1 Press the **search** button.

 3 Type a **word** or **number** to search for.

 2 Choose a **field** to search.

EXAMPLE: Which planets or moons orbit Jupiter?

For this one, I need to search the **orbits** field, and I'm going to search for "**Jupiter**" in that field.

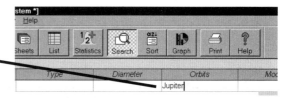

Use > and < for greater than and less than

> < means "less than"   < = means "less than and including"
> > means "greater than"   > = means "greater than and including"

(On some programs, you have to put = > or = < instead of > = and < =)

EXAMPLE: Which planets and moons are smaller than the Earth?

 1 I need to search the **diameter** field because diameter is a measure of size.

 2 The Earth's diameter is 12756 km. So I need to search for "**< 12756**".

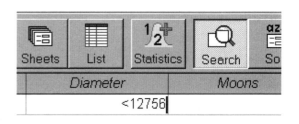

EXAMPLE: Which planets have 2 or more moons?

 1 The field is easy this time, it's the **moons** field.

 2 I need to search for "**> = 2**" which means "greater than and including 2".

Databases

① Fill in the blanks to complete these searches.

Q: How do I find planets and moons that are hotter than 100 °C?

A: Press search, click on the _temperature_ field and type _> 100_.

Q: How do I find the planets and moons that are colder than 15 °C?

A: Press search, click on the .... field and type ....

Q: How do I find the planets and moons that are larger than 10000 km in diameter?

A: Press search, click on the .... field and type ....

Q: How do I find the planets and moons that are 500 km or smaller in diameter?

A: Press search, click on the .... field and type ....

② What is a moon?

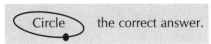 the correct answer.

It's like a small planet which orbits a planet instead of the Sun. We (Earth) have one moon which we call "the Moon".

It's something round that is made out of cheese.

③ What does orbit mean?

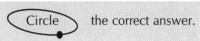 the correct answer.

Orbit means "go up"   Orbit means "go round"

Orbit is a special type of sherbet that makes you float.

PRACTISE SEARCHING A DATABASE

- Open a database and search for a **word** or **number**
  E.g. In a countries database, you could search for countries in **Africa**.
  Or in a minibeast database, you could search for creatures with **8 legs**.

- Now try some > and < searches
  E.g. In a countries database, search for countries with a population **less than 1 million**.
  Or in a minibeasts database, you could search for creatures with **more than 10 legs**.

AND and OR Searches

If you want to do really clever searches, you'll need to use the search words AND and OR.

AND finds when two things are true

 Find planets and moons which are warmer than -50°C, but colder than 100°C.

 The Temp field shows the surface temperature.

 The temperature needs to be greater than -50 °C **AND** less than 100 °C

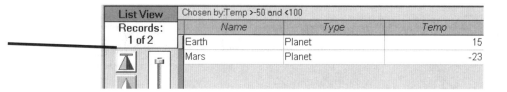

 So the search is > -50 **AND** < 100. And it goes in the Temp field.

I've found 2 matches — Earth and Mars.

List View	Chosen by:Temp >-50 and <100		
Records: 1 of 2	Name	Type	Temp
	Earth	Planet	15
	Mars	Planet	-23

OR finds when either thing is true

 Find all the moons that orbit Mars or Pluto.

 I need to search the Orbits field.

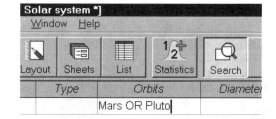

And the search is **Mars OR Pluto**.

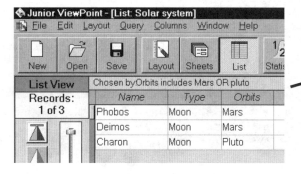

I've found 3 matches for this: Mars has two moons called Phobos and Deimos. And Pluto has one moon called Charon.

AND and OR Searches

① Help me with this search...

I want to find planets or moons that are between 1000 km and 5000 km in size (diameter).
Draw a circle around the correct search.

Diameter
>1000 AND <5000

Diameter
<1000 AND >5000

Diameter
>1000 OR <5000

② Help me to find the rocky and icy ones...

Which search should I do to find planets and moons with rocky or icy surfaces?

A
Surface	
rocky OR icy	

C
Surface	
rocky AND icy	

Some planets don't have solid surfaces — Jupiter and Saturn are just huge balls of gas. Weird, huh...

B
Name	
rocky AND icy	

D
Surface	
fish fingers	

The search I need to do is ....

③ I want all the moons that orbit Saturn and Jupiter.

Which of these fields should I search?   **Name   Orbits   Surface   No of moons**

What should I type in it? ....

④ Some of these are real moons, some are English villages.

Can you guess which are which? Draw a little moon beside each real moon.

Kiddlington

Oberon

Enceladus

Callisto

Umbriel

Ophelia   Cleadon   Tamworth   Broughton

Unit 5B — Using Complex Searches

AND and OR Searches

Sometimes you'll want to search for words in two different fields.

Searching in two different fields is easy

All you do is type a word to look for in each field you want to search.

 Which moons have icy surfaces?

 I need to search the type field for "moon".
The type field says if it's a planet or moon.

 And I need to search the surface field for "icy".
The surface field says what the surface is made from.

 Then I choose whether it's an AND search or an OR search.

I only want records which are moons **and** are icy

— so I want the AND search.

And here are the results: I found 4 moons with icy surfaces.

If I'd done an **OR** search, the computer would find all the moons and all records with icy surfaces.

And I'd end up with 35 matches like this:

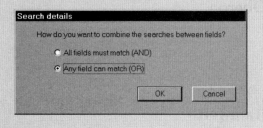

AND and OR Searches

① *Complete these sentences by writing AND or OR.*

.... searches find records matching **both** search words.

.... searches find records matching **either** search word.

② *Help me choose a small moon to buy.*

When I win the lottery, I'm going to **buy a moon** *(just a small one)*.
How can I find a moon smaller than 15 km in diameter on my database?

tick
☐

Type **"moon"** in the type field,
type **"< 15"** in the diameter field.
Do an **AND** search.

tick
☐

Type **"rabbit"** in the type field,
type **"15"** in the diameter field.
Do an **AND** search.

Type **"moon"** in the type field,
type **"15"** in the diameter field.
Do an **OR** search.

tick
☐

③ *Which planet or moon would make a good ski resort?*

If I have any lottery money left, I want to
make an icy planet or moon into a **ski resort**.

Which of these searches will find **icy** planets or moons which
are **warmer than -100 °C**? *(People won't come if it's colder than that!)*

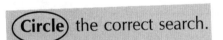

Moons		Surface
	100	twiglets

	Surface	Temp
	Icy	>-100

	Surface	Temp
	Icy	-100

PRACTISE AND AND OR SEARCHES

Go and try some AND and OR searches. If you have a space database, you could try
the searches on these pages. In a countries database, you could search for countries in
Europe with an area **smaller than 1000 square kilometres**. In a materials database,
you could search for materials that let **heat** or **electricity** move through them.

 **Computer Activity**

Search a database

For this activity, you will need our Goatsaudition database which you can download from our website at **http://www.cgpbooks.co.uk/goats/goat.htm** (It'll only take a few seconds to download). You can download it in any of these formats: Junior Viewpoint, Microsoft Access, Microsoft Excel, csv, txt (csv and txt files will work on any database program).

In this project you will:

Choose people to star in the new West End musical, "Goats".

I've written a musical called "Goats"

It's set in Ireland.

There are 4 main characters — Paddy (the goat-keeper), Brian (the goat), Sinead and Katy.

I have a database of people who have auditioned

30 people have auditioned to be in my musical. Their auditions have been recorded in the **auditions** database. You are going to find **four main characters**, **four singing sheep** and **eight rollerskating goats**.

"a musical extravaganza!"   *"it'll be bigger than Phantom of the Opera!"*   *"it's got goats in it!!!"*

"Goats" Cast list:

Paddy: _____   Brian: _____

Sinead: _____   Katy: _____

The Sheep: **The Goats:**

_____   _____   _____

_____   _____   _____

_____   _____   _____

_____   _____   _____

This is the empty cast list for my play.

You are going to complete this list by finding people from the database.

Search a database
Computer Activity

Find the four main characters:

The four main characters must be really good at **acting**, **singing** and do good **Irish accents.**

1. First of all, find the people who can sing and do good Irish accents.

> *Search for **> 7** in the singing field and **=good** in the accent field.*
> *You need to do an **AND** search because you want both things to be true.*

How many people have you narrowed it down to?   .... people

> The most important thing is **how well they can act**.
> So now you need to **choose** the ones who can act the best.

2. Go to **list view** so that you can see all of your results together.

Use the **Sort** button to put the remaining people in **order** of how well they can act.

> *Press the **Sort** button, then select the **acting** field.*

3. Choose the **two** best boys and the **two** best girls.

They will be the main characters.   **Write their names on the cast list**

Find the rollerskating goats:

You need to find **8 people** to play rollerskating goats:

1. Search the database to find rollerskaters.

> *Search for **=very good OR = excellent** in the rollerskating field.*
> *This will find people who are either very good or excellent rollerskaters.*

2. Choose the 8 best dancers from the list you have. *Don't choose anyone you've already picked!*

They will be the rollerskating goats.

Write their names on the cast list

Finally, do your own search to find 4 singing sheep:

The singing sheep must be girls and their singing score (out of ten) must be **7 or greater**.
Search the database to find the best girls.
Write down your search here.   ....

The sheep should be small, so pick the
four smallest girls from your results to play the sheep.   **Now go and complete the cast list!**

Unit 5B — Using Complex Searches

Searching the Internet

The Internet is a bit like a database. A really really huge one.

Use "search engines" to find stuff on the Internet

Search engines are the best way to find stuff on the Internet.

I want to find information
about football, so I type
football here and press Search

We found 526 web sites matching your search:

1   USA Today - American Football
    The big story that everyone is talking about...

2   NFL news
    Dallas Cowboys, Chicago Bears, San Francisco 49ers, find out the latest...

3   NFL - National Football League
    The number one site for lovers of American football...

EEK! — Most of the websites it is
finding are about American football...
I HATE AMERICAN FOOTBALL!!

AND and OR searches work on the Internet

I'm going to try an **AND** search to find
websites about UK football.

We found 427 web sites matching your search:

1   FIFA World Cup 2002
    The Latest World Cup news from Japan...

2   Liverpool Football Club
    The unofficial site of the UK's best football club...

3   UK Fantasy Football
    The best fantasy football site on the net - kick here...

AH, THAT'S BETTER
— putting UK *(for "United Kingdom")*
has worked. Now all the websites
are about UK football. Phew!

Searching the Internet can be annoying

There's loads of information to find on the Internet, but...

 It takes ages to find things
You'll often have to try lots of different searches until you find the stuff you want.

 A lot of it is rubbish
Anyone can make a website, so you can't always trust what you do find.

Searching the Internet

① What can you use to find things on the Internet?

Draw a big exhaust pipe on the correct answer.

⟹ **Like this**

search and replace

map and compass

jet engine

search engine

② Draw lines to match each search to the correct description

chocolate **OR** igloo

chocolate **AND** igloo

chocolate **AND NOT** igloo

"chocolate igloo"

Finds websites containing the word **chocolate** or the word **igloo**.

Finds websites containing the word **chocolate** but not the word **igloo**.

Finds websites containing the phrase **chocolate igloo**.

Finds websites containing the word **chocolate** and the word **igloo**.

③ How do I open the Destiny's Goat website?

A Click here

We found 526 web sites matching your search:

1 KYLIE MINOGRE
http://www.kylieminogre.co.bla/bla/bleurgh
I'm spinning a goat, can't goat you out of my head, ... loads of Mp3s to download

2 DESTINY'S GOAT HOMEPAGE
http://www.destinysgoat.bla/bla/bleurgh
Gossip, Lyrics, Goat pics, MP3s and much more

3 GOATS OFFICIAL SITE
http://www.rollergoatsmusical.blabla/bla/bleurgh
Meet the stars of the West End's hottest new musical, Goats.
Exclusive interviews, pictures, cast info, sound clips and much more...

B Click here

DON'T CLICK HERE!

Answer ....

④ Why is searching on the Internet annoying?

....

....

....

Computer Activity — Search on the Internet

In this project you will: *Do fancy searches on the Internet to find really cool stuff*

Connect to the Internet

1. Connect to the Internet (you must **get permission** before doing this).
2. Go to a search engine. Ask your teacher or parent which one to use.
   (*Or use this one: **www.yahooligans.com***)

> ### Before you start searching, here's a few tips:
>
> Most (but not all) search engines let you do **AND** and **OR** searches.
>
> Putting **speech marks** round a phrase *"like this"* tells the search engine to look for that **exact phrase**.
>
> Some search engines **automatically** do AND searches if you type in more than one word.

Find some *tasty* recipes:

I want to find a nice **dessert recipe that uses apples**.

1. Try out each of the searches below. Then say what kind of results you got.

Search:	*Do you find any good websites? What were they?*
recipe OR apple	....
recipe AND apple	....
"apple recipes"	....
dessert AND apple	....
dessert AND recipe	....

type this into your search engine and press the SEARCH button

Did you find recipes and were they the right ones?

2. If you found a good recipe, **print it out or save it**.
3. Now go back and try searching for a different recipe.
   You could look for **cake recipes that use banana** or **trifles with kiwi fruit**.

Search on the Internet  Computer Activity

Find some good jokes or poems

1. Choose **one** of these things to look for.

A poem about spiders

Some "doctor doctor" jokes

A poem about school

Jokes about bats

2. Write down **three** Internet searches you could try.
Use **AND** in one of them.
e.g. **poems AND school**

Search:

❶ ....

❷ ....

❸ ....

3. Now **try** each of the searches and see what you get. Hopefully, you'll find some good jokes or poems. If you don't, try a **different search** (or a different **search engine**).

4. When you find a really good poem or joke, **print it out.** (You could test the joke on your friends and see if they laugh.)

Finding historical facts:

Henry VIII ("Henry the Eighth") was a very famous king of England.

Search the Internet for information about Henry VIII and use it to complete this information sheet.

You could try these searches:
King Henry
"Henry VIII"
"Henry the eighth"
"Henry VIII" AND facts

Name: King Henry VIII (Henry the Eighth)
Reigned from .... to ....
Number of wives ..6....

Name of wife	How did she die?
Anne Boleyn	Head chopped off

Draw a picture of him in this box:

Finished? Phew. Well done, you're now an Internet searching *expert.*

Uses of Databases

Databases are really useful for storing and sorting information — like names, words, numbers and times. You can also use databases to draw charts and graphs. These can make the information easier to read. Don't worry — you've seen them before...

You can display databases in different ways

1 Here's a record card for a doctor's patient. It's a way to view a database

The Doc's Medical Practice

Patient's Medical Record

Name: Chris P Bacon

Date of Birth: 15/10/89

Sex: Male

Allergies: Hayfever

Major Illnesses: ChickenPox, Tonsillitis

2 The information from the record cards is entered into a database.

3 Then you can view loads of record cards at once — using a list view, like this.

Name	Allergies	Date of Birth	Sex	Major Illnesses
Chris P Bacon	Hayfever	151089	Male	Chicken Pox
Hugo First	None	90788	Male	None
Teresa Green	Animals	261178	Female	Mumps
Terry Fied	None	130265	Male	Shingles
Lou Swires	None	41294	Female	None
Eileen Dover	None	100451	Female	Diabetes

Databases are used in loads of different places

Banks store information about customers (like how much money they've got) on databases .

Schools have databases about their pupils (containing information about number of days off, age, average test mark, and so on...).

Doctors store information about their patients (history of illnesses, allergies and things).

Uses of Databases

① Name three things databases are useful for.

1. ....

2. ....

3. ....

② Name two different ways of displaying databases.

1. ....

....

....

2. ....

....

....

Doctor, doctor, I feel like a database.

How long have you been feeling this way?

Search me.

③ Can you think of three places where databases are used?

1. ....

2. ....

3. ....

Errors in Databases and the Internet

Even the simplest mistake in a database can cause a lot of problems.

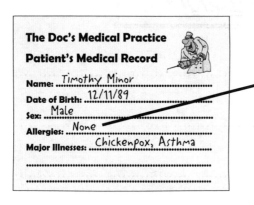

Timothy Minor has hay fever, but his doctor has made a mistake — he hasn't written it down. So Timothy has no tablets and a runny nose.

The Internet is full of information — but some of it's biased

Books have editors to make sure everything's correct. But there's no one to do that on the Internet — anyone can put information on it — so not all of it is correct.

The Internet is a bit like a massive database — it has loads of information. It also has loads of errors.

Some information is biased. That means it's for or against something. Like a site called "Books are great" might be biased in favour of books. Here are a couple of biased sites:

My mate Eleanor thinks the Earth is flat. She's even made a website about it. So if you read about the Earth on the Internet, you might read that it's flat.

This is Brian's website — he reckons his dad's car is the fastest in the world ever. (It's not really — it's rubbish). One day I searched on the Internet for the fastest car, and Brian's dad's came up.

These are some ways errors get on the Internet — don't think that everything you read is true.

Errors in Databases

① What kind of problems might be caused by a database error?

First **think of a database**, then think what could happen if a record had a mistake in it.

....

....

....

② Design a webpage with information that is wrong.

Try to think of something **wacky** but make it look like it's **serious**, not a joke.
Look back at the examples on the opposite page if you're stuck.

Database Errors

There are THREE types of error

Name: Gordon Caine

Age: Nine years old

Year: 5

Hair Colour: Brawn

Eye Colour: Brown

Worst Food: Onions

Favourite Food: Mobile phone

Wrong field type.
That means using words when it should be numbers — or the other way round. It's easy to see what it should be, so it's easy to correct.

Spelling or typing mistake.
It's usually easy to see what it should be, so it's usually easy to correct.

Silly data.
It's difficult to see what it should be, so it's difficult to correct.

When errors are really hard to correct, you might have to delete the whole record.

Different errors cause different problems

From	To	Departure Time	Arrival Time
Ulverston	Foxfield	11.18	12.06
Ulverston	Foxfield	13.36	14.23
Ulverston	Foxfield	16.04	16.55
Ulverston	Foxfield	14.18	19.06
Foxfield	Ulverston	9.09	9.58
Foxfield	Ulverston	11.22	12.11
Foxfield	Ulverston	13.46	14.32
Foxfield	Ulverston	19.43	20.36

This looks like a typing mistake. It should probably be 18:18.

Here are some problems this error could cause:

1. People won't know there is a train at 18:18.
2. There isn't a train at 14:18 — but passengers might try to catch it.
3. People might not even go to Ulverston because there's no evening train back.

This database stores details of people using an Internet e-mail site. If the password or username is wrong, the users won't be able to log on and use their e-mail.

Username	Password	Name	Country
gordoncainee	ridiculous	Gordon Caine	England
damo	likewhile	Damian Paul	England
ricemaker22	itsnotlike	Alex Diment	Australia
tightfoot	oldapples	Gavin Lightfoot	England
wanderer	burndenpark	Peter Gaskell	England
mcdoo	tax	Chris MacCandles	Northern Ireland
flanderson	workworkwork	Gavin Anderson	Scotland
pelling	lazylazy	Charlie Pelling	England

Database Errors

① *Practise spotting errors in databases.*

There are 6 mistakes in each of these database sheets.

Circle each mistake.

I bet you can't do it quicker than my mate Andy... he only took 45 seconds.

Name	Age	Year	Hair Colour	Eye Colour	Favourite Food	Worst Food
Rita Milkmaid	9	Four	Blonde	Blue	Sausages	Cabbage
Desmond Barrow	8	4	Brown	Brown	Apple pie	Pork crackling
Vera Childs	10	6	Brown	Blue	Ice crem	Fish
Julia Saint	Six	1	Red	Blue	Dog food	Chips
Mary Older	11	6	Blonde	Blue	Scrambled egg	Onion
Jo-jo Loner	7	3	Brow	Green	Runner Beans	Cheese
Loretta Martin	9	4	Black	Brown	Steak	Nuts
Billy Shears	5	1	Blonde	Fish	Sausages	Sprouts

Superhero Name	Super Powers	Super Weaknesses	Super Favourite Colour
Super Pointing Finger Man	5th Feb 1948	Scared of mittens	Silver
Stinkman	Stickman	189732	Brown
Mr. Muffin	Everything he touches turns into a muffin	Water pistols	Brown
Magnificent Maria	Her pants can turn into a parachute	Fear of oysters	Turquoise
Super Bath Wader	Can turn into a rubber duck	Can't turn back	Cleaver Girl
Super Karate Chgop Man	Super Karate Chop	Only an inch tall	Black
Cod Man	Big lips/supersuck	Waterbound	Yes
Cleaver Girl	Chop-chop hands	Allergic to Itching powder	Grey
Jam Jar Jim	Can put anyone inside a jam jar	Can't fasten jam jar lids	Red
Helen Haddock	Batters everything	Hates Fresh salad	Orangey-Brown

PRACTISE CORRECTING ERRORS

Ask your teacher to give you a database with errors in.

Now see if you can **spot the errors**. **Correct** each error if you can.

If you don't know what it should be, you'll just have to **delete** it.

Explain the problems that could be caused by the errors that you spotted.

....

....

....

Databases

Errors can be really hard to spot

The table below shows Brian's height at different birthdays.

There's an error in it — but it's very hard to spot.

The answer is upside down at the bottom of this page.

Brian's Birthday Height Chart

Birthday (in years)	1	2	3	4	5	6	7	8	9	10	11	12	13
Height (in cm)	75.6	91.4	99.0	106.7	111.8	102.7	124.5	129.5	135.3	140.3	145.4	149.9	154.9

Drawing a graph can help you see errors more easily

Here is a line graph of the table above.

The error is much easier to spot using the graph.

Any kink in the line could be an error.

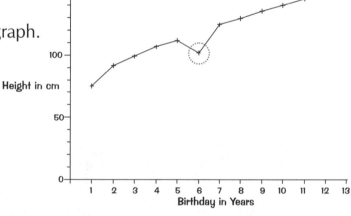

Brian's Birthday Height Graph

Line graphs are for continuous data

Line graphs should only really be used for continuous data.

Continuous data changes smoothly, like temperature or someone's height.

People don't suddenly jump from 140 cm to 155 cm — they grow through all the values in between.

If you used a bar chart, it would look silly — as if people suddenly became bigger.

The height for 6 years should be 118.7 cm

Databases

① Which of these makes database errors easier to spot?

☐   1. A pair of binoculars

☐   2. A line graph

☐   3. Mr. Larry Lebowski, the Private Detective from Brooklyn, New York.

② What should line graphs be used for?

1. What type of data should line graphs be used for?

....

2. Give three examples of this kind of data.

a)   ....

b)   ....

c)   ....

③ Spot the error on this graph.

Circle the point on the graph that you think is most likely to be an error.

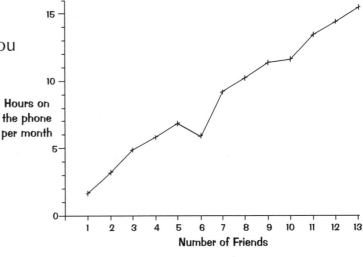

 **Computer Activity**

Database Project

 *Find and correct errors in a database*

You will enter information into a database, and use a variety of methods to find errors.

Create a database and enter information

Here's a database about Clara's first 13 years.

Age in years	Height in cm	Weight in kg	Favourite food
1	73	9	Mashed bananas
2	89	13	Spaghetti Hooops
3	998	15	Strawberry Yoghurt
4	106	17	Shepherd's Pie
5	112	19	Ice Cream
6	117	31	Ice Crem
8	122	24	Ice Cream
8	129	27	Chocolate Sponge
9	135	31	Sticky Toffee Pudding
10	141	35	Syrup Sponge
11	149	39	Football
12	154	42	Steak
13	156	46	Chocolocolate

1. Create a new database.
2. Enter this information about Clara into a database. This is a list view so each row is a different record card.

> Make sure you use the right field type. That means using number fields for numbers, and word fields for words. Obvious really.

Print out the database and search for errors

1. Print out your database. (Go to the "File" menu, and then "Print".)
2. Check it for errors. And remember there are three types of error.

There are quite a few errors in the database. Some of them are dead easy to spot, and some are as hard as finding fun in maths.

Three types of error
1. Silly data
2. Wrong field type (number not word, word not date etc.)
3. Spelling or typing mistakes.

Database Project

Draw a line graph to help you spot errors

1. Press the **Graph** button.

> Some databases will look a bit different from this, but they all work in a similar way.

2. Choose **Line Graph**.

3. Choose which **fields** you want to use.

4. Hit the **Plot** button.

Look for a kink or wiggle in the graph. That's where you usually find errors.
The bigger the kink, the more likely it is to be an error.

Correct the mistakes you find

1. Try to correct any mistakes you find.
2. Some mistakes will be too hard to correct. Delete the whole record if they are.

> *Look on page 38 for tips on correcting errors.*

Save your database

1. When you've made the corrections, save your database.
2. Write the filename of your database here:

Budgets

Budgets show how someone plans to spend money.

Budgets are Lists of Things You Need to Buy

I've invited some monsters round for tea. I have £42 to spend on food and drink.
This is my budget — it shows how I plan to spend my money.

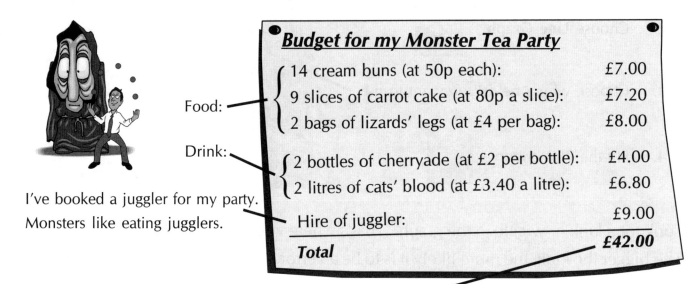

Food:

Drink:

I've booked a juggler for my party.
Monsters like eating jugglers.

Budget for my Monster Tea Party

14 cream buns (at 50p each):	£7.00
9 slices of carrot cake (at 80p a slice):	£7.20
2 bags of lizards' legs (at £4 per bag):	£8.00
2 bottles of cherryade (at £2 per bottle):	£4.00
2 litres of cats' blood (at £3.40 a litre):	£6.80
Hire of juggler:	£9.00
Total	**£42.00**

The bottom line shows what I spend <u>altogether</u> — it's the <u>total</u> of all the costs.

Budgets Sometimes Have to Change

I need to change my budget. There are 3 reasons:

1. Oggie the ogre tells me he hates carrot
   cake, and would prefer more cream buns.
2. Cats' blood is on offer at the supermarket
   this week — just £1.20 a litre.
3. I also have to invite Britney the Banshee.
   She doesn't eat much, but likes cherryade.

This means I have to change my budget. I need more cream buns and more cherryade,
but less carrot cake. I'll save money on cat's blood, but I still only have £42.

Computers are Great for Budgets

There are two main reasons why computers are great for doing budgets on.

1. Computers can calculate things <u>really quickly</u>.

2. You can <u>change</u> your budget and see the effects <u>straight away</u>.

Budgets

① Work out this budget.

The local witches' group is having its yearly party. They have to be careful with their money. Fill in the gaps to show what they spend on dinner.

Witches' Yearly 'Night to Howl' Budget

2 newts' eyes at £2 an eye ....

3 small frogs' tongues at £1.30 a tongue ....

8 bats' claws at 90p a claw ....

20 large rabbits' feet at £2 a foot ....

4 metres of snake at £1.70 a metre ....

Total ....

② How long will it take you to do this question?

The budget for the witches' party has to change.
How much will the party cost now?

Time yourself doing this question — go on...

Newts' eyes are on special offer: only £1.30 each.
5 frogs' tongues are needed, not 3.
Bats' claws suddenly increase in price to £2.30 a claw.
Small rabbits' feet are better value — so get 30 of these at £1.20 instead of the larger ones.
The price of snake falls to £1.20 a metre.

Time taken: ....

(This question would take about 15 seconds on a spreadsheet — honest.)

③ Give 2 reasons why computers are great for budgets.

1. ....

2. ....

....

Spreadsheets

Spreadsheets are fantastic for doing things like budgets.

Spreadsheets Have Loads of Cells

A spreadsheet has lots of boxes arranged in rows and columns. Each box is called a **cell**. Just click on a cell and type — that's what goes into the cell.

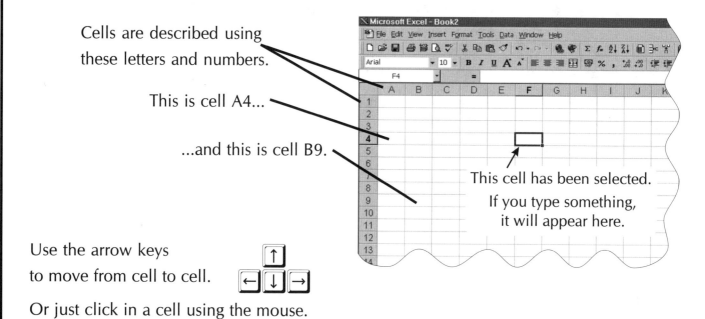

Cells are described using these letters and numbers.

This is cell A4...

...and this is cell B9.

This cell has been selected. If you type something, it will appear here.

Use the arrow keys to move from cell to cell.

Or just click in a cell using the mouse.

Adjust the Rows and Columns

Spreadsheets are great for loads of things. I've made a table of my friends' favourite hobbies. But some of the columns are too narrow.

1) Columns B and C are too narrow.

2) It's impossible to read some of the information.

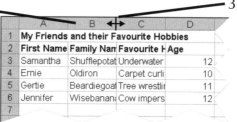

	A	B	C	D
1	My Friends and their Favourite Hobbies			
2	First Name	Family Nam	Favourite H	Age
3	Samantha	Shufflepotat	Underwater	12
4	Ernie	Oldiron	Carpet curli	10
5	Gertie	Beardiegoal	Tree wrestli	11
6	Jennifer	Wisebanan	Cow impers	12
7				

3) But if I move the cursor halfway between the two letters, it changes shape...

4) ...and I can change the width of a column by dragging it.

It's much better like this:

	A	B	C	D
1	My Friends and their Favourite Hobbies			
2	First Name	Family Name	Favourite Hobby	Age
3	Samantha	Shufflepotato	Underwater disco dancing	12
4	Ernie	Oldiron	Carpet curling	10
5	Gertie	Beardiegoat	Tree wrestling	11
6	Jennifer	Wisebanana	Cow impersonations	12
7				
8				

Try this:

Double-click between row or column labels instead — the columns should become the perfect size.

Spreadsheets

① Match the cells to their contents.

Draw lines to show what each of the cells in this database contains.

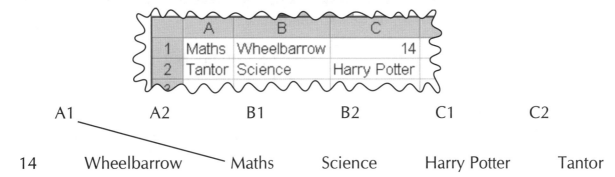

	A	B	C
1	Maths	Wheelbarrow	14
2	Tantor	Science	Harry Potter

A1   A2   B1   B2   C1   C2

14   Wheelbarrow   Maths   Science   Harry Potter   Tantor

② Where will the text appear?

In which cell will the text appear if I type 'Obi Wan'?

....

③ Which cell do I move to?

If I press this sequence of keys, which cell will be selected? (Start from the cell selected in the picture.)

↑ → ↓ → ↑ ← ←

....

MAKE A SPREADSHEET FOR A YUMMY DESSERT

Think of a really nice **dessert** like **sweetcorn trifle** or **lemon and cabbage cake**.
Make a spreadsheet which shows all the **ingredients** your dessert would
need and how much each ingredient would **cost**.
So for a <u>trifle</u> you would need things like jelly, sponge, cream, custard...
Or for a <u>cake</u>, you'd want things like flour, eggs, sugar...

*Look in a recipe book if you get stuck. If you don't know how much things cost,
have a guess (or have a look when you go to a supermarket).*

Calculations on a Spreadsheet

You can do a lot more on a spreadsheet than make tables.

Spreadsheets are Great at Doing Calculations

Spreadsheets can hold different kinds of information.

(1) A cell can hold <u>text</u>...

(2) ...<u>numbers</u>...

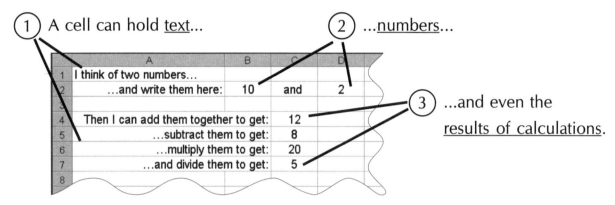

(3) ...and even the <u>results of calculations</u>.

* The main reason why spreadsheets are fantastic is because they can do calculations.

* Type any number you like into a cell, and the spreadsheet can use it in a calculation.

* It can then take the result of a calculation and use it in another calculation.

* You can have thousands of different calculations in a spreadsheet.

Working Out a Budget is Easy on a Spreadsheet

I've entered my monsters' tea party budget onto a spreadsheet.

(1) The numbers in column D show how many of each thing I need...

(2) ...Column E shows the price of 1 item...

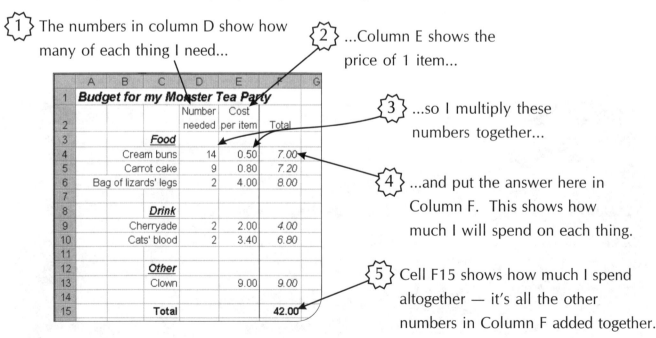

(3) ...so I multiply these numbers together...

(4) ...and put the answer here in Column F. This shows how much I will spend on each thing.

(5) Cell F15 shows how much I spend altogether — it's all the other numbers in Column F added together.

There are lots of calculations here. But spreadsheets are great for doing calculations.

Calculations on a Spreadsheet

① Name 3 types of information a spreadsheet can hold.

1. ....   2. ....

3. ....

② Which of these would a spreadsheet be useful for?

Draw a (sausage) around the things that you could use a spreadsheet for.

Calculating the cost
of holding a party.

Mending your
bike's puncture.

Working out how much your
Christmas presents will cost.

Removing wax
from your ears.

Doing the
washing up.

③ This is what I had for dinner last night.

The spreadsheet below shows how much I spent on last night's dinner.
Complete the sentences using words from the jaggedy box.

Column D   adding

cost   text

number   multiply

	A	B	C	D
1	What I had for dinner last night:			
2		How many?	Cost for 1 item (£)	Total cost (£)
3	Steak pie	1	1.70	1.70
4	Sausage flans	2	1.35	2.70
5	Baked potatoes	7	0.90	6.30
6	Cream cakes	14	0.10	1.40
7	Pineapples	2	0.58	1.16
8	Cups of coffee	8	0.90	7.20
9			Total	20.46

1. The name of each type of food is in Column A — this information is ....

2. Column B contains the .... of each type of food I ate.

3. The .... of 1 of each type of food is in Column C.

4. To calculate what I spent on each type of food, I
   .... the number in Column B by the number
   in Column C, and put the result in ....

5. Cell D9 contains the total cost of my meal — I find this
   by .... cells D3-D8.

Formulas

Spreadsheets are great at calculations. Let the spreadsheet know you want it to calculate something by using a **formula**.

Enter Formulas Using an Equals Sign '='

Get the spreadsheet to calculate something by using a formula.
A formula starts with an equals sign (=).

This spreadsheet adds two numbers together.

- I want to add the numbers in cells C1 and C2.

  - I want the answer in cell C3.

    - So I click on C3, and type:

Don't forget the
equals sign (=).

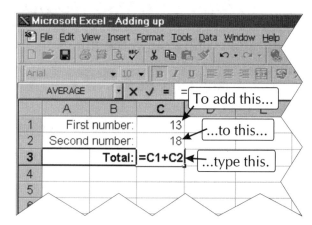

Instead of typing 'C1', I can just click on the cell.
The computer writes 'C1' in my formula automatically.

Change What's in a Cell Using the Formula Bar

Editing what's in a cell is easy. You can change numbers, text or formulas.

⟨1⟩ Click on a cell — its contents appear in the formula bar.

⟨2⟩ Click in the formula bar and edit things in the normal way.

⟨3⟩ Press 'Enter' when you finish.

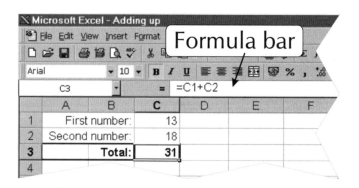

If you want to see what formula is in a cell, click on it and look in the formula bar.

Spreadsheets Change Answers Automatically

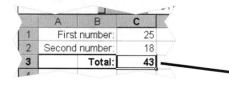

Spreadsheets are dead clever.

If I change the number in cell C1 to 25, the answer in cell C3 changes automatically. It's like magic.

Formulas

① What would I type to add these numbers?

I want to add these 2 numbers. Which of these formulas do I need to type?
Circle the correct answer.

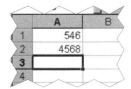

	A	B
1	546	
2	4568	
3		
4		

=C1+C2   =A1+A2

A1+A2   =A1+B1

② Write down the correct formulas.

There are four pairs of numbers in this spreadsheet.

I want to add each pair and put the result in the shaded cell.

Write down which cell I need to click in, and what I need to type for each sum.

	A	B	C	D
1				
2	(a)	88	52	
3				
4				
5	(b)	542	(c)	654
6		2423		545
7				
8				
9				
10	(d)	54	12	

(a) Click in cell .....**D2**..... and type .....**=B2+C2**...

(b) Click in cell .... and type ....

(c) Click in cell .... and type ....

(d) Click in cell .... and type ....

GO AND PRACTISE ENTERING FORMULAS

Copy out the spreadsheet in question 2 and put in your formulas.
Check your formulas by seeing if you get the same answers on a
calculator (or if you're good at adding, just check them in your head).

Making Predictions

When you change a number or a formula in a spreadsheet, all the calculations are done again — really quickly. It's a good way to test how good you are at maths.

Test Yourself by Changing a Formula

This spreadsheet takes two numbers and adds them together.

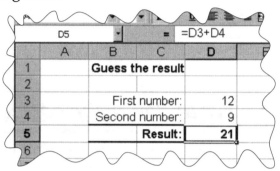

- Change the numbers in D3 or D4.

  Try to guess what the answer in D5 will be before you hit 'Enter'.

  - Test how good you are at <u>subtraction</u>.

    Cell D5 contains the formula: `= D3 + D4`

    Change this to `= D3 – D4`

    Say what you think the answer will be before you hit 'Enter'.

Use * and / to Multiply and Divide

Computers don't use the normal multiply and divide signs: × and ÷.
Instead they use * for multiply and / for divide.

Important:	Computers use * instead of ×, and / instead of ÷.

Make your Spreadsheets Look Nice

Spreadsheets are pretty clever — but you can make them look pretty too.
This can make things easier to understand as well.

- These two spreadsheets do exactly the same thing.

- But the version on the right is a lot clearer, and looks nicer too.

I've made some text **bold** and some *italic*, and spaced the cells out a bit.

If you want to make it look *really* funky, you can also change colours and fonts with these buttons.

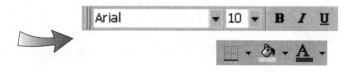

Making Predictions

① What are the multiply and divide symbols?

What symbols do computers use for multiplication and division instead of × and ÷?

× .... ÷ ....

② What will the answers be?

Look at the numbers and formulas in these spreadsheets. What will the answers in cell A3 be?

a.

	A
1	12
2	7
3	=A1+A2

b.

	A
1	3
2	5
3	=A1*A2

c.

	A
1	45
2	3
3	=A1/A2

d.

	A
1	15
2	7
3	=A1-A2

....

③ Make a 'Maths Testing Machine'.

This is the 'Maths Machine' from opposite. You can change the numbers
in cells C3 and C4 and try to guess the answers before you hit 'Enter'.
What formulas do you need in cells A8, B8, C8 and D8?

A8: ....

B8: ....

C8: ....

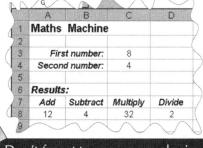

	A	B	C	D
1	Maths Machine			
2				
3	First number:		8	
4	Second number:		4	
5				
6	Results:			
7	Add	Subtract	Multiply	Divide
8	12	4	32	2
9				

D8: ....

Don't forget to use an equals sign.

What would the answers in A8-D8 be if you swapped the numbers in C3 and C4?

A8: .... B8: .... C8: .... D8: ....

Now go and check your results using a real spreadsheet.

Using Brackets

This looks hard at first, but it isn't really. You might even have seen this stuff in maths before. But that means it's unlikely to be much fun.

Computers Multiply Before They Add

Computers multiply and divide things before they add or subtract anything.

	A	B
1	3	=A1+A2*A3
2	4	
3	5	

The formula in B1 is confusing at first — it looks as though there might be 2 possible answers.

 Will the computer add A1 to A2 to get 7...

...and then multiply the answer by A3 to get 35?

 Or will it multiply A2 by A3 to get 20...

...and then add A1 to the answer to get 23?

But computers <u>never</u> get confused like this.

Computers do **all multiplications and divisions before any addition or subtraction**.

So the answer in B1 will be **23** — multiply A2 by A3, and add A1 to the result.

But Computers Do Anything in Brackets First

You can use <u>brackets</u> to make sure a computer does what you want it to.

Add 1 to your number...
...and multiply the answer by 2.

I want to use this rule on the number in cell A1.

I can't use the formula '=A1 + 1*2' — the multiplication will be done first and I'll get the wrong answer.

To do the addition <u>before</u> the multiplication I have to use <u>brackets</u>.

The 'add 1' bit is in brackets, so that's done first...   **=(A1 + 1)*2**   ...and then the answer is multiplied by 2.

If you get an answer that you weren't expecting, check whether you need brackets.

Brackets look a bit like an unfinished sausage...

$= (A1 + 4)*4 \implies = (A1 + 4)*4$

...just remember you have to do the bit in the 'sausage' first.

Using Brackets

① What does a computer do first? Tick the correct box.

- ☐ Multiplication and division.
- ☐ Addition and subtraction.

② What difference do the brackets make?

Write down the answers that will appear in cells A3 and C3.

a.

	A	B	C
1	18	6	3
2			
3	=A1-B1*C1		=(A1-B1)*C1

A3: ....   C3: ....

b.

	A	B	C
1	24	6	3
2			
3	=A1/B1-C1		=A1/(B1-C1)

A3: ....   C3: ....

c.

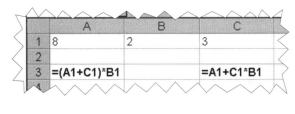

	A	B	C
1	8	2	3
2			
3	=(A1+C1)*B1		=A1+C1*B1

A3: ....   C3: ....

d.

	A	B	C
1	2	6	12
2			
3	=(B1+C1)/A1		=B1+C1/A1

A3: ....   C3: ....

③ What will the answers be?

Write down the answers that will appear in the five cells containing formulas.

A3: ....

A5: ....

	A	B	C	D
1	8	2	5	4
2				
3	=A1*(B1+C1)/D1		=(A1+B1+C1)*D1	
4		=D1-A1/B1+C1		
5	=C1-B1+A1+D1		=C1*D1/(A1+B1)	
6				

B4: ....   C3: ....   C5: ....

Now go and check your results using a real spreadsheet.

Sums

Spreadsheets can do a lot more than add two numbers together.

Use SUM to Add Lots of Numbers Together

This is a list of things I want to buy people for their birthday.

	A	B	C	D
1	Person	Present	Cost in £	
2	Dave	Woolly hat	3.50	
3	Stuart	Slippers	6.00	
4	Taissa	Oil paints	9.00	
5	Jo	Lampshade	4.50	
6	Cathy	Poetry book	5.75	
7		Total		
8				

C7 =

✸ I need to put a formula in cell C7 to work out how much all these presents will cost.

✸ I could use:

$$= C2 + C3 + C4 + C5 + C6$$

✸ But a quicker way is to use:

$$= SUM(C2:C6)$$

Five Things About Using SUM

SUM adds together a whole column of numbers. But you need to know how to use it.

① Start with an equals sign.

② First cell you want to add...

③ ...last cell you want to add.

=SUM(C2:C6)

④ Don't forget the brackets...

⑤ ...or the colon (the two dots) in the middle.

You Can Add Rows of Numbers Too

The numbers don't have to be in a column. They just have to be next to each other. This is a spreadsheet to show how much it rained one week.

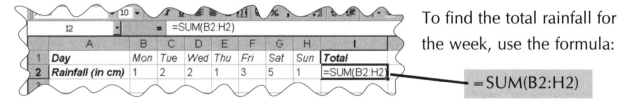

	A	B	C	D	E	F	G	H	I
1	Day	Mon	Tue	Wed	Thu	Fri	Sat	Sun	Total
2	Rainfall (in cm)	1	2	2	1	3	5	1	=SUM(B2:H2)

I2 = =SUM(B2:H2)

To find the total rainfall for the week, use the formula:

$$= SUM(B2:H2)$$

Good things about SUM: 1. It's a lot quicker.
2. You're less likely to make a mistake.

Sums

① What formula do I need?

This is my budget for the costumes and props for the local pantomime.

Circle the formula I need to put in cell B9 to work out the total cost.

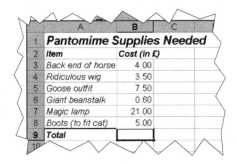

	A	B	C
1	**Pantomime Supplies Needed**		
2	Item	Cost (in £)	
3	Back end of horse	4.00	
4	Ridiculous wig	3.50	
5	Goose outfit	7.50	
6	Giant beanstalk	0.60	
7	Magic lamp	21.00	
8	Boots (to fit cat)	5.00	
9	Total		

SUM(B3:B8)   =SUM(B3-B8)

=SOME(B3:B8)

=SUM(B3:B8)   =SUM B3:B8

② Work out my golf score.

I played golf at the weekend. I didn't play very well.

Write down the formula I need to put in cell K2 to add up my score for the first 9 holes.

Use the SUM command.

	A	B	C	D	E	F	G	H	I	J	K
1	Hole	1	2	3	4	5	6	7	8	9	Total
2	Score	6	8	12	9	6	25	7	52	111	

....

③ Use SUM in your answers to these questions.

This spreadsheet shows the sales of petrol by a garage in one week.

(a) What formula do I need to put in cell E4 to calculate the total for Tuesday?

....

(b) What formula do I need to put in cell C10 to calculate the total for the afternoons?

	A	B	C	D	E
1	**Sales of petrol (in £)**				
2		Morning	Afternoon	Evening	Total
3	Monday	1080	1026	604	2710
4	Tuesday	835	803	815	
5	Wednesday	1451	1546	714	3711
6	Thursday	866	1630	1068	3564
7	Friday	1508	774	1243	3525
8	Saturday	1940	1258	1463	4661
9	Sunday	1815	1005	1264	4084
10	Total	9495		7171	

....

(c) Write down a formula I could put in cell E10 to calculate the total for the week.

....

Now go and check your results using a real spreadsheet.

 **Computer Activity**

Make a Budget

You'll need a spreadsheet program for this project — e.g. Microsoft Excel.

In this project you will:

Work out a budget for a class party.

If you do this project **really well**, your teacher will let you have the party.

You'll need to: ✓ Carry out a survey to decide what food people will want to eat.

✓ Calculate a budget for the party using a spreadsheet.

The Survey — What will be most popular?

- You need to work out what food people will want to eat at the party.

- Write down some questions for everybody in the class to answer.
  They might be something like these.

---

1. What is your favourite kind of sandwich? ....

2. What would you like to drink at the party? ....

3. What is your favourite crisp flavour?
   ☐ Salt and vinegar   ☐ Cheese and onion   ☐ Beef   ☐ Prawn cocktail
   Other (write it here) ....

4. Are you vegetarian?   Yes / No

Graphs — Decide what you need to buy.

- When everybody has answered the questions, look at the results and decide what will be most popular.

Bar charts

- It's a good idea to draw graphs. You could draw a bar chart or a pie chart.

- Once you know <u>what</u> to buy, you have to decide <u>how many</u> of each item you need.

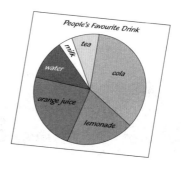

Pie charts

Make a Budget

Set up your spreadsheet.

Your spreadsheet might look something like this:

> Work out how many loaves/packs/bottles you'll need and put it in this column.

> Get this information from old receipts, or by visiting a nearby shop.
>
> (Remember: 80p would be 0.80.)

> Add formulas here to calculate the total cost of 4 loaves of bread etc.
>
> (Hint: you'll need to multiply 2 numbers together.)

> Add a formula here to find the total cost.
>
> (Hint: use SUM.)

	A	B Packs/bottles needed	C Price for 1 pack/bottle (in £)	D Total cost
1	**Budget for Class Party**			
2	Food			
3	Bread for sandwiches	4	0.80	
4	Cheese	2	1.45	
5	Ham	5	1.90	
6	Chicken	3	2.10	
7				
8	**Drink**			
9	Cola	2	1.20	
10	Lemonade	1	1.20	
11	Orange juice	3	1.30	
12	Milk	1	0.40	
13			*Total*	

Are you within budget?

- **Add a formula** to work out how much each person in the class will have to pay.
  (Hint — you'll need to divide your total by the number of people in the class.)

- If the cost is **too high**, then you'll have to change some numbers.
  Maybe you can buy less orange juice, or buy cheaper cheese.

Make your spreadsheet look great.

You can easily change the way things look in your spreadsheet.

Select one or more cells and use these buttons:

 Use **bold**, *italic* or underlined text.

 Put the text in the left, right or centre of the cells.

 Change the colour of the text in each cell.
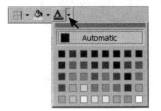

 Change the colour of each cell.
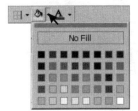

 Change the outline of each cell.
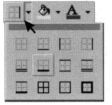

Time for the party!

It's time to ask your teacher if you've done well enough to deserve a party. Good luck!

Instructions

Some things need a Single Instruction to work

① Put your ticket in the machine...

② ...and the barrier rises — fantastic.

The only instruction in this is "Raise the barrier".

Some things need a Sequence of Instructions

This pelican crossing works using a sequence — it uses more than one instruction.

One changes the traffic lights. One changes the pedestrian lights.

The button needs to be pressed to start the sequence.

① Push the button... → ② ...and the traffic lights go red and stop the cars... → ③ ...then the green walking man will appear — so walk.

Instructions

① Which of these use a sequence of instructions?

Tick the ones which use a sequence of instructions.

☐ A Pelican Crossing

☐ A Kitten

☐ An Aunt

☐ A Level Crossing

☐ A Chicken Curry

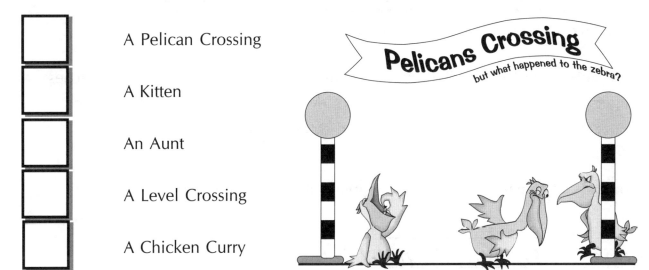

Pelicans Crossing
but what happened to the zebra?

② Put this sequence for a level crossing into the right order.

I've done the first one and the last one for you...

The train goes past   *1*

The lights start flashing   *2*

A train approaches   *3*

The lights turn off   *4*

The gates go up   *5*

The gates go down   *6*

③ Why did the pelican cross the road?

For some fowl reason...

Inputs and Outputs

You can make your own programs to control things with a computer. You might use a control box too.

You Need a Control Box to Make Things Work

Control boxes connect the computer to outputs or inputs.

Outputs include things like lights, speakers, motors, buzzers, etc...

Inputs include things like buttons, switches and levers, as well as temperature, light and sound sensors...

outputs do things

inputs get information

Connect a Light to Output 1

Plug a light bulb into output 1.

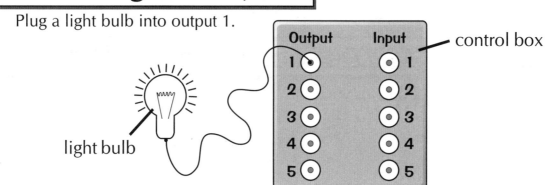

light bulb

control box

Control Languages are in Charge of Control Boxes

To turn on your light, enter "turn output 1 on" into your control program.
Enter "turn output 1 off" into your control program to turn the light off.

You might have to write something a bit different, like "switch output 1 on". Your teacher will know about this.

If the light was connected to an output other than 1, you'd use that number instead (e.g. if it was connected to output 3, you'd write "turn output 3 on").

This is how you turn outputs on and off when you're using flow charts.

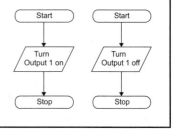

Outputs

① Control your outputs.

The sentences below should be about controlling outputs.
Fill in the gaps using the words in the box on the right.

get information switches
do things control box lights

Outputs and inputs are connected to a ....

Speakers, motors and .... are outputs. Outputs ....

Buttons, ... and levers, and temperature, light and sound sensors

are all inputs. Inputs ....

② Wake up Grandpa.

Grandpa is sleeping as usual. I've chosen three things I could use to wake him.
I've put them next to him and connected them to a control box.
Below is a list of control language commands.
Tick the command that is most likely to wake Grandpa.

Output 1
Monster Hifi

☐ Turn output 1 off

☐ Turn output 3 on

☐ Turn input 1 on

☐ Turn ouput 1 on

☐ Turn output 2 on

Output 3
Tacky Digital Clock → 14:34

Output 2
Puny Lamp

③ Turn these things on.

Write what you would type to turn these outputs on.

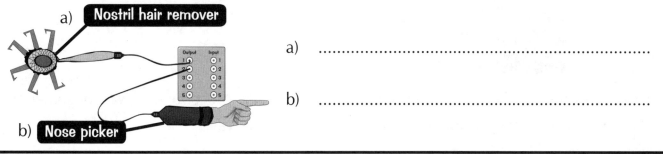

a) **Nostril hair remover**

b) **Nose picker**

a) ....

b) ....

Repeat and Wait

Flash your lights

Now you know you can turn a light on and off using a control language.

Do that again and again and you've got a flashing light.

This is where the "Repeat" command comes in handy.

You learnt about "Repeat" last year, when you used LOGO and turtles.

"Repeat" makes things happen again.

So you might write:

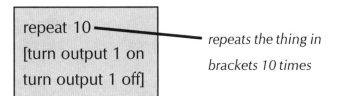

repeat 10 — *repeats the thing in*
[turn output 1 on   *brackets 10 times*
turn output 1 off]

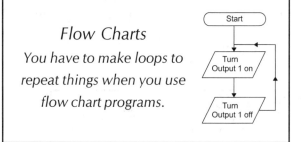

Flow Charts
You have to make loops to
repeat things when you use
flow chart programs.

Use the DELAY (or WAIT) command

The command in the grey box above just makes the lights flash really really quickly.

It would be better for the lights to stay on for longer and off for longer. This is where the "Delay" (or "Wait") command is useful.

So you might write:

repeat 10
[turn output 1 on
delay 1 ————— *waits for 1 second*
turn output 1 off
delay 1] ————— *waits for 1 second*

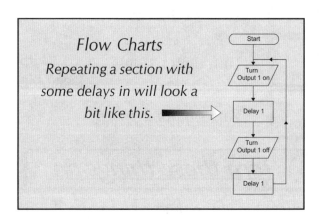

Flow Charts
Repeating a section with
some delays in will look a
bit like this.

This procedure is called "Flash". It's a good idea to name procedures so you or someone else will know what they do. There's less confusion that way.

Repeat and Wait

① Write a program to sound a buzzer.

A buzzer is connected to output 1. Make a flow chart using these boxes so that the buzzer keeps sounding for short bursts.

(You don't need all the boxes...)

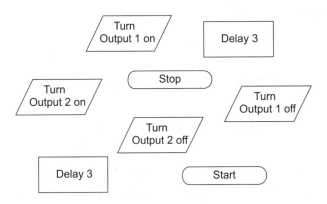

② Write a program to flash a light.

A light is connected to output 2.

Make a flow chart using these boxes so that the light flashes (but it's on for longer than it's off).

(Again, you don't need all the boxes...)

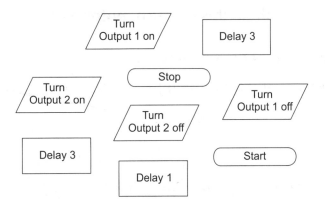

NOW TRY YOUR PROGRAMS OUT FOR REAL...

Time for the fun bit... Go and **try out your programs**.

You'll need to connect a **buzzer to output 1** and a **bulb to output 2** of your control box.

Then **type your instructions** from the flow chart into your control program. Once you've got both programs working, you could try writing one program which does **both things**.

Motors

Motors can go Backwards and Forwards

A motor is a type of output which moves something. You can write programs to control one.

Motors use three commands:

1) to move them one way

2) to move them the other way

3) to turn them off

They'll probably look a little like this:

turn motor a fd ———————— *This will move something forward*

turn motor a rev ———————— *This will move something backwards*

*(saying "motor **a**" is like saying "output **1**" — it selects a particular motor (there could be loads — "motor b" to "motor z"...)*

You Have to Turn Motors Off After You Use Them

- Turning a motor on makes it move, but it won't stop running until you turn it off.

  - So, you need to write a command that will do this — **"turn motor a off"**

- You'll also need a "Delay" command — otherwise the motor will just switch on then switch off straight away.

  - *(Some software programs will also let you control the speed of the motor.)*

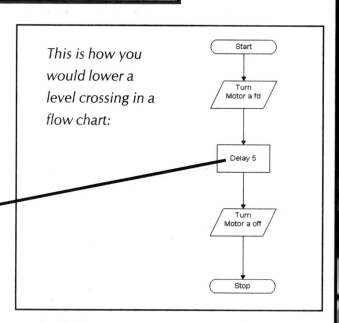

This is how you would lower a level crossing in a flow chart:

Start

Turn Motor a fd

Delay 5

Turn Motor a off

Stop

Motors

① Write a program to make this pig fly backwards.

Use these objects to draw a flow chart
that will make my electric pig fly backwards
for 10 seconds. The motor for his wings is
controlled by **Motor a**.

(Stop)

/ Turn
Motor a off /

[Delay 10]

(Start)

/ Turn
Motor a rev /

② Write a program to lower and raise a level crossing.

Use these objects to make a flow chart.
The level crossing is controlled by **Motor b**.
*(Hint — you'll need delays to keep the crossing
closed while the train goes by, as well as delays
while the motor is running.)*

/ Turn
Motor b rev /

[Delay 5]   (Stop)

/ Turn
Motor b fd /   / Turn
Motor b off /

[Delay 10]

[Delay 5]

(Start)

/ Turn
Motor b off /

Controlling Lots of Outputs

You Can Control More Than One Output at a Time

You can deal with different outputs **at the same time** — e.g. you could write a program that turned off a guinea pig cleaner at the same time as it turned on a cat stirrer.

You just type in...   **turn output 1 off**

                             turn output 2 on   ...and it happens.

Storyboards can Help You Plan Programs

It can start to get tricky when you have lots of outputs to think about. Writing a **storyboard** will help you understand **which commands** need to be written into your program.

This is what a traffic light storyboard might look like:

| Red | → | Amber | → | Green | → | Amber | → | Red |

BUT — you can be more precise, and write in **exactly** when each light goes on and off.

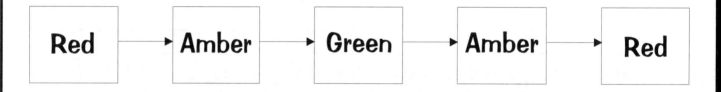

| Red On | Delay 8 | Amber On / Red Off | Delay 3 | Green On / Amber Off | Delay 8 | Amber On / Green Off | Delay 3 | Red On / Amber Off |

(this may not be how all traffic lights work, but this is about a magic traffic light, and magic traffic lights are simpler than ours...)

The first bits of this program could be written like this:

Red = Output 1
Amber = Output 2
Green = Output 3

    turn output 1 on
    delay 8
    turn output 2 on
    turn output 1 off
    delay 3 etc...

This is what the flow chart would look like...

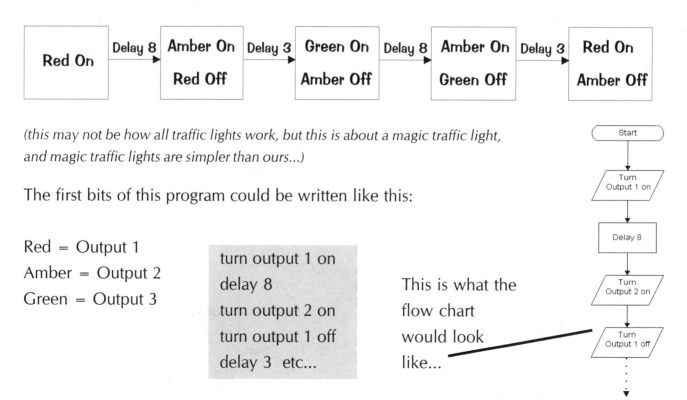

Controlling Lots of Outputs

① Draw a circle around the correct commands to:

Turn my electric pig (output 1) on at the same time as my electric moose (output 2), but while turning off my toaster (output 3).

turn output 2 on
turn output 3 on
turn output 1 off

turn input 1 on
turn output 2 on
turn output 3 off

turn output 1 on
turn output 2 on
turn output 3 off

② Write the program for the magic traffic light.

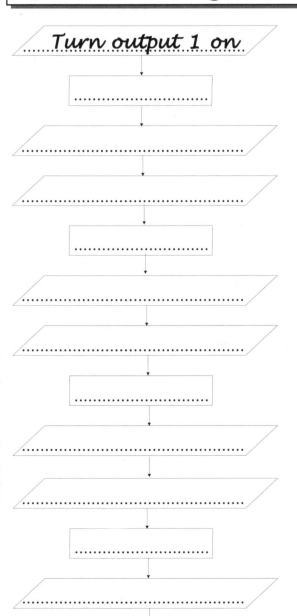

Turn output 1 on

Write a flow chart that will turn the magic traffic light to red, go through the sequence once, then change back to red again.

Use the storyboard on the opposite page as a guide.

Remember: Red = Output 1
Amber = Output 2
Green = Output 3

TEST YOUR TRAFFIC LIGHT PROGRAM

Now it's time to try out your program on the computer. **Connect 3 bulbs** to the control box. You'll have to pretend that they are the bulbs of a traffic light. Now **test your program**. It might not do exactly what you expected. If it doesn't, find out what's wrong and **fix it**.

Breaking Into Sections

Split your Programs into Sections

Another way to avoid confusion is to write **procedures** for each **section** of your program. This will make it:

— easier to understand
— easier to change bits

e.g. a pelican crossing could have
a **procedure** for each of these sections:

Hey — didn't you say that pelicans could have a Mini?

No — and that's not a Mini anyway, is it?

What do I know? I'm just a pelican...

"normal"	"walk"	"flash"
Traffic is moving normally	Traffic stops and pedestrian walks	Lights flash before sequence ends and returns to "normal"

"normal" — Traffic lights are green. Little man is red.

"walk" — The "Wait" button is pressed by a pedestrian. The traffic lights go amber then red. The little man goes green.

"flash" — The little green man flashes. The traffic lights flash amber. The little man turns red. The traffic lights turn green.

Each section has its own name too, to make them easier to keep track of...

> Your computer program might call procedures **"Sub-Programs"** or **"subs"**. Don't worry — they're still the same thing...

You Can Repeat Each Section

You can repeat these procedures as many times as you like by adding a "repeat" command. You might write:

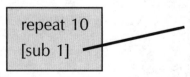

repeat 10
[sub 1]

"sub 1" means the same as saying "run procedure 1".
This might change depending on what program you use.

In some programs, you might enter the name of your procedure instead.
Your teacher will be able to tell you more...

repeat 10
[flash]

Breaking Into Sections

① _Write the storyboard for a procedure._

Write a storyboard for the "walk" section of the pelican crossing program —
shown on the opposite page. Use the instructions below to fill in the boxes.

delay 8

delay 2

green light off
amber light on

little red man
goes green

amber light off
red light on

"wait" button pressed

② _Write your storyboard into a procedure._

Use your storyboard and the list of outputs below to help you. You can write a flow chart,
or a procedure in your control language. Call it "walk".

"Wait" button = Input 1

Red = Output 1
Amber = Output 2
Green = Output 3

Little red man = Output 4
Little green man = Output 5

③ _How do you get an angry pelican into a Mini?_

....

....

Problems Caused by Errors

You can write procedures to control as many different inputs and outputs as you like, but this is really useless if you leave important bits out or type something daft...

The Program Only Does What You Tell It To Do

A program will only work if you write it correctly. It's not like a human being.
— this is **good** because it follows orders and doesn't get distracted
— this is **bad** because it can't make its own decisions and solve unexpected problems.

If you give a command to start doing something (like turning on a heater) you MUST remember to tell it when to stop heating (or else the school explodes...) (on the other hand...).

Oh... If only Heather had remembered not to let the school explode...

So, you have to be really careful not to leave any commands out.

Check all the commands are there and that the lines that link them are in the right place.

Be As Organised As Possible. Always. Absolutely Always.

The keys to all this are planning and double-checking everything.

Test what you've written before you use the procedure for real.

It gets easier if you keep everything as organised as possible.

THE GOLDEN RULE IS:
NEVER START SOMETHING
YOU CAN'T FINISH...

They told me to wait here.
That was 3½ centuries ago...

Problems Caused by Errors

① _Give one good and one bad thing about controlled devices._

Good: ....

Bad: ....

② _What's wrong with this flow chart?_

This program will put food in my dog's bowl at lunchtime while I'm out. It's also set to ring a buzzer while the food pours, so that my dog wakes up.

Something's wrong with it though — in the spaces provided, write down what the problem is and how I can fix it.

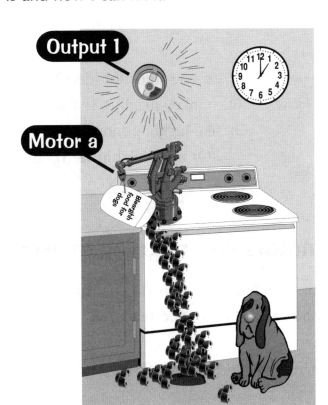

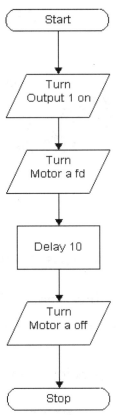

Problem: ....

Solution: ....

 **Computer Activity**

Procedures Project

In this project you will:

Write procedures to control a fairground display

You're going to design a sign to advertise a fairground attraction. The sign will have lights, buzzers and motors. You're going to write the procedures to make them work...

Choose something to advertise:

Pick a fairground show, ride or stall that you want to advertise.
It can be anything that can be advertised on a sign.
I'm choosing "The Bearded-Snake Tent".

(Are you stuck for ideas?
How about monkey-juggling seals?
Or seal-juggling monkeys?
Or a fish'n'chip van?)

Decide how many outputs and motors you're going to use:

I'm going to use three lights, a buzzer and a motor — the motor's going to control a motorised snake that moves backwards and forwards as if it's going to bite you.

Write in the boxes below how many outputs and motors you're going to use.

Lights ☐

Buzzers ☐

Motors ☐

Procedures Project

Computer Activity

Draw a sketch of what your display will look like:

This is a rough design of what I want my display to look like. I've labelled all the outputs and motors clearly.

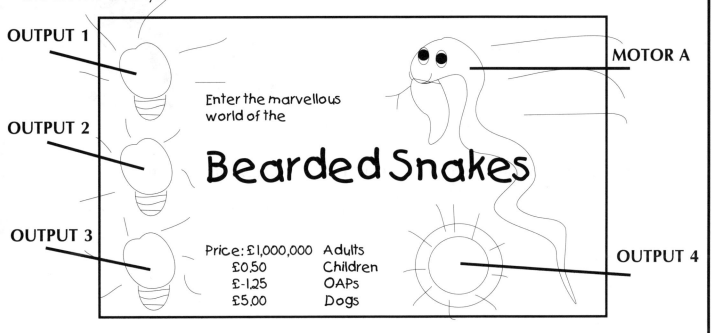

Now draw yours in the box below, and be sure to label all your outputs and motors:

 **Computer Activity**

Procedures Project

Split your display into sections:

Think about breaking your display into easy chunks.
You'll be able to write a mini-procedure for each one.

e.g. mine splits easily into 3 sections:

  — lights

  — buzzer

  — motor (for snake)

I have to give each a name, so I'll call them "lights", "buzzer" and "snake".

Write the names of each of your mini-procedures into these boxes (use as few or as many as you like):

1	**2**	**3**
4	**5**	**6**

Write a storyboard for each section:

Now write up each storyboard carefully.

Make sure you label each storyboard, so you know which section it's about.

e.g. I want my three lights to come on one by one, then all come on together at the end. This is what my "lights" storyboard looks like...

Lights

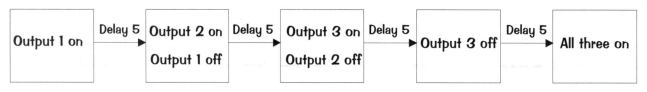

Output 1 on	Delay 5	Output 2 on Output 1 off	Delay 5	Output 3 on Output 2 off	Delay 5	Output 3 off	Delay 5	All three on

Procedures Project

Write each storyboard into a procedure:

You know how to do this now, so what I'm going to say is quite dull — You just need to remember to keep everything as organised as possible.

Ho ho ho...

DOUBLE-CHECK EVERYTHING...

Use this list to help you a little:

- Make sure you haven't left any commands out.

- Check that all the commands are in the right order.

- Check the delays are the right length.

- Make sure you've turned the motors off after using them.

Putting it all together:

All that's left to do now is write the final procedure that links up all your mini-procedures. Mine looks like this:

```
start
repeat 5
[lights]
repeat 5
[buzzer]
[snake]
stop
```

That's about it really.
Hope you didn't mind all the snakes...

Machines for Monitoring

Machines can monitor things like temperature, noise levels, sound levels and so on. This is useful in loads of different ways.

Monitoring Happens Every Day

Weather forecasters need loads of accurate information — temperatures and wind speeds, for example.

1. They need a lot of measurements from lots of different places.

   Machines are used which automatically take measurements at regular intervals.

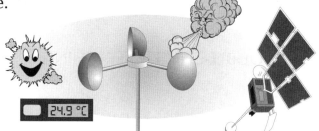

2. Central heating in houses uses a <u>thermostat</u> that monitors a room's temperature.

   If the temperature falls, the heating is turned on.

   If the temperature gets too high, the heating is turned off.

Anything that actually measures something is called a <u>sensor</u>.

Machines Can Monitor Where People Can't

This could be because the measurements are needed from places that are hard to get to.

Or because they are needed over a very short period...

Like the light levels during an explosion — measuring these could be dangerous as well.

...or over a very long period.

Like outside temperatures — important for weather forecasting.

Machines for Monitoring

① Name 3 different things a computer can monitor.

1. ....   3. ....

2. ....

② Where are machines used for monitoring?

Give 2 situations where machines are used for monitoring.

1. ....

2. ....

③ What's a device that measures something called?

....

④ Why are machines used for monitoring?

Give 3 reasons why it's sometimes better to monitor using a machine and not a person.

1. ....

2. ....

3. ....

In what other ways do machines monitor the environment?
Think of as many as you can.

Presenting Results

Once the data's been recorded, someone's got to look at it and work out what it means.

Sometimes it's Good to Draw a Graph

The most basic way to present the information is in a <u>table</u>.
This table shows how many cabbages I ate last week.

But it's a bit boring, and it's not easy to see
patterns — or readings that might be interesting.

Day	Number of Cabbages I ate
Monday	21
Tuesday	22
Wednesday	24
Thursday	25
Friday	26
Saturday	88
Sunday	29

I've drawn some cabbages round this table to
make it less boring. But it's still quite dull.

Patterns and odd readings are much easier to see if you <u>plot a graph</u>.

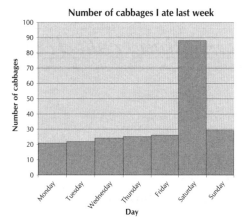

It's much more obvious that I'm
eating more and more cabbages.

And that something weird
happened last Saturday.

Computers are good for making tables and graphs — it's as easy as eating cake.

Line Graphs are Best for Continuous Data

There are different kinds of graphs that computers can draw.
Norris my flying pig took off just before 1 pm yesterday and landed just after 7 pm.

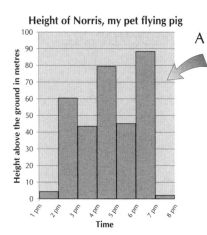

A <u>bar chart</u> of his height makes
it look as though Norris
'jumped' between heights.

In fact, his height changed
<u>continuously</u> during his flight
— so a <u>line graph</u> would be better.

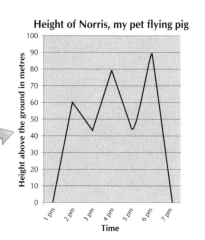

Presenting Results

① Which are ways to present readings from sensors?

Circle the correct answers.

In a table   With a spoon   On a line graph

On a bed of fresh lettuce   As a bar chart

② Plot these results as a bar chart.

This table shows the number of full turns my hamster did in his treadmill last week.
Draw a bar chart to show the results.

Day	Number of Turns
Monday	160
Tuesday	590
Wednesday	240
Thursday	280
Friday	320
Saturday	330
Sunday	350

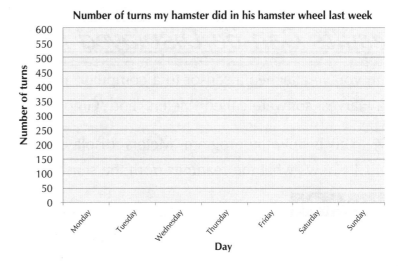

③ Make a cup of tea but don't drink it.

Which of these two graphs showing the temperature of a cup of tea is more realistic?
Tick the correct box, then explain your answer.

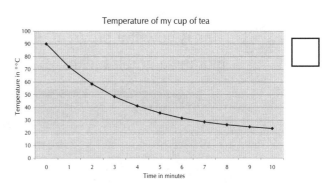

Reason: ....

....

Monitoring Software

Computers are great for showing results. But the thing that actually measures sound levels, temperatures and so on is called a <u>sensor</u>. You can attach sensors to a computer.

Attaching sensors to a computer

Different kinds of sensors measure different things.
You can usually attach more than one sensor to a computer at a time.

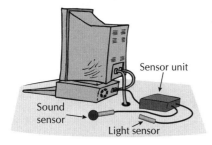

Sensor unit

Sound sensor

Light sensor

The sensors might be attached to a
sensor unit that you plug into the computer.

One sensor might measure <u>sound levels</u>.

Another might measure <u>light levels</u>, or the <u>temperature</u>.

Results Can be Displayed in Different Ways

When you've attached a sensor to a computer, it's easy to display the results. I'm using Data Harvest software called '<u>Meters</u>' and '<u>Graph</u>'. But other software is pretty similar.

 This is how the program '<u>Meters</u>' displays results.
It shows what the readings from the sensors are <u>now</u>.

Light meter

39

Units

Max. 47 Units
Min. 39 Units

This <u>digital</u> meter gives
the reading as a number...

...and this <u>analogue</u> meter
has a moving 'needle'.

Temperature meter

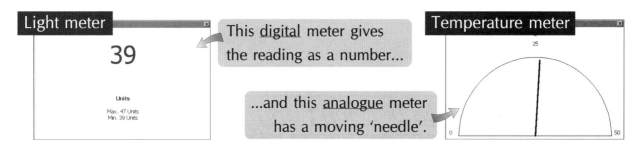

To use a different sensor in '<u>Meters</u>', double-click the meter.

 This is how the program '<u>Graph</u>' shows the readings from the sensors.
Plotting a graph means you can see how things have <u>changed</u>.

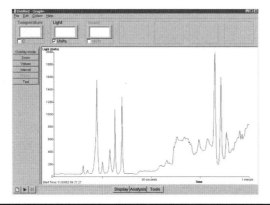

'Graph' is a much more useful
program, as it lets you collect
data over a period of time.

Monitoring Software

① What's the usual way to attach a sensor to a computer?

Draw a (sausage) around the correct answer.

Push the cable carefully into the floppy disk drive.

Loop the cable around the keyboard and tie a granny knot to secure it.

Plug the sensor into a box attached to the computer.

② Show results using meters or graphs.

What's the basic difference between using a meter and a graph to display your results? Complete the following sentences using words from the cloud.

> changed   meter   now   useful   period

A .... shows what the reading from one of the sensors is

.... A graph is usually more .... , because all

the readings taken during a certain .... of time can be shown.

This means you can see how the readings have ....

③ What equipment would you need?

Someone's asked you to measure whether schoolchildren are noisier when they are hot or cold. Which of these things would be useful?

☐ Light sensor   ☐ Dictionary   ☐ Graphing software   ☐ Sound sensor

USE A SENSOR TO MONITOR THE SOUND IN YOUR CLASS

This activity is a good one for the whole class to do together.

Connect a **sound sensor** to the computer. Set up your monitoring program to **make a graph** of the **sound** in your classroom (your teacher will help you with this). Record yourself being **silent**, **talking** quietly and **shouting**. Print out a **graph** of your results. Can you tell on which parts of the graph you were being silent, talking and shouting?

Datalogging

Datalogging means <u>measuring</u> something over a period of time and <u>recording</u> the readings you get. It's not hard. In fact, most software makes it pretty easy.

Use 'Graph' for Datalogging

For datalogging, you need a program that can record results over time — like Data Harvest 'Graph'. But even if you use something different, it will probably work something like this.

1 Click on the 'New' button to record new data.

2 A window then pops up.
Make sure that 'Real time' is selected.

See page 88 for more about 'Remote'.

3 Now decide how long you want to collect data for.
(Click 'Continuous' if you want to collect data until you press the 'Stop' button.)

4 This is how often a reading will be taken...

...but you can take a reading whenever you press your mouse button if you'd prefer — just click 'Snapshot mode'.

You can change this with some software, but not all.

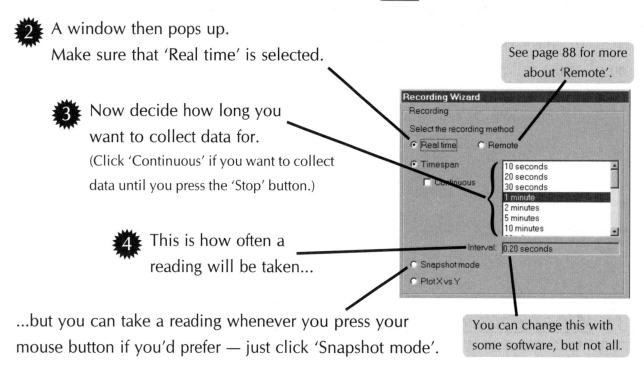

5 Now you have to say which sensors you want to use to collect data.
Just tick the boxes on the left.

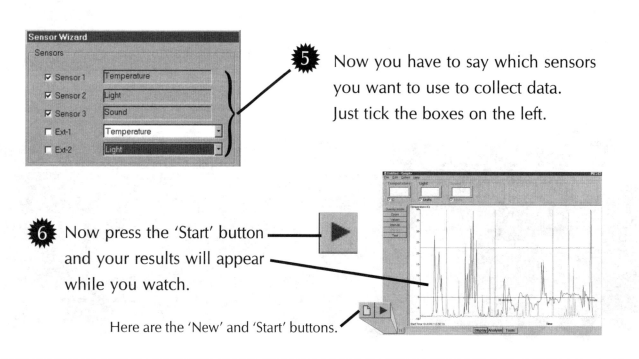

6 Now press the 'Start' button and your results will appear while you watch.

Here are the 'New' and 'Start' buttons.

Datalogging

① What does 'datalogging' mean?

....

....

② Which program do you need to use for datalogging?

Which of these could you use to display data collected over a period of time?
Tick the correct answer.

☐ Graph   ☐ Meters

③ Complete this passage to show how you collect data.

Use words from the box.

> how long   Start   between   New   sensors
> Continuous   Snapshot   Real time

1. First you have to press the '..' button.

2. Then make sure '..' is selected.

3. Next, you have to decide .... to collect readings for.

4. If you want to carry on recording data until you tell the computer to stop, click on

   '..'.

5. Sometimes you can choose the time .... readings, but some
   software will decide this for you.

6. If you want, you can tell the computer to take a new reading whenever you press a
   mouse button — to do this, click on '.. mode'.

7. Next, you have to select which .... to use.

8. The computer starts to take readings when you click on the

   '..' button.

Datalogging Software

Change Datalogging Settings if You Need to

You need to decide how long to monitor something for — it all depends.

✹ If you're recording something that changes very slowly, it's a good idea to take measurements over a long period of time.

✹ And if something's changing very quickly, you need to take measurements very close together.

Stanley's recording his armpit temperature, but it changes very slowly — so he'll be there a while yet.

Draw Different Kinds of Graphs

Most software will let you display your results in different ways.

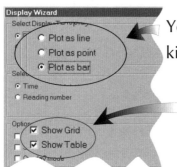

You can draw different kinds of graph...

...and show a table of results, or a grid behind the graph.

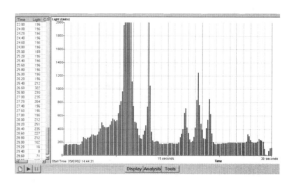

And Make Your Graphs Easy to Understand

Labelling a graph makes it much easier to understand.
Use the 'Text' and 'Title' tools.

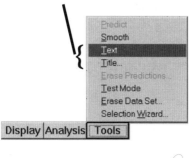

GRAPH OF

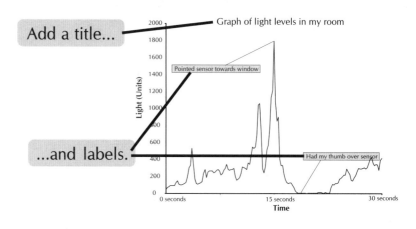

Add a title...

...and labels.

Graph of light levels in my room

Pointed sensor towards window

Had my thumb over sensor

Datalogging Software

① *How long do you have to collect readings for?*

Circle the correct words to make these sentences correct.

1. The (**slower** / **quicker**) something changes, the (**longer** / **wheelbarrow**) you should collect data for.

2. The (**elephant** / **quicker**) something is changing, the (**closer together** / **further apart**) you need to take your measurements.

② *Do these change quickly or slowly?*

Decide whether each of these changes quickly or slowly.

Draw hare's ears in the box if it changes quickly, but a tortoise shell if it changes slowly.

1. Someone's body temperature.

3. Light levels from a TV.

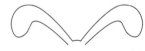

2. Sound levels as someone talks.

4. Temperature of a normal room.

You could check your answers using sensors and monitoring software.

③ *What does this graph show?*

Tick the correct box.

- [ ] Noise levels as I walk to school.

- [ ] Midday temperature ouside my back door last summer and autumn.

- [ ] Height of Brendan, my pet bat, as he flew around the garden last night.

- [ ] It's impossible to say, as there are no labels on the graph.

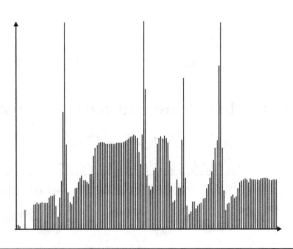

Unit 5F — Monitoring the Environment

Collecting Data Remotely

Collecting data '<u>remotely</u>' means taking a sensor away from a computer to collect results. You could record the temperature outside, or collect data on traffic noise levels.

Sensors can be Used Away from the Computer

This isn't hard at all really. All you do is click a button and go off to the Sahara Desert.

* Press the 'New' button, and click on 'Remote'.

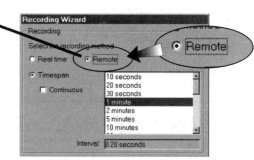

* Decide how long to collect data for, and which sensors to use — this is the same as on page 84.

* Now you can unplug the sensors and take them to the middle of the Sahara Desert to collect your data. Just press a button to start collecting data.

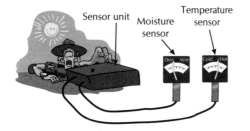

* All the measurements are stored in the sensor unit.

* You have to transfer them to the computer later.

Download the Data When You Get Back

When you get back from the Sahara, you have to transfer your measurements to the computer. This is called '<u>downloading</u>'.

* Connect the sensor unit to the computer.

* Then click on the 'Collect Remote Data' button.

All the data's transferred into the computer, and automatically plotted on a graph.

<u>Check with your teacher before you go to the Sahara Desert.</u>
This is especially true if you're taking equipment that belongs to the school.

Collecting Data Remotely

① Give 2 advantages of collecting data remotely.

1. ....

2. ....

② Circle the correct word in each of these sentences.

1. To collect data remotely you have to tick the box marked (**Remote** / **Stay at home**).

2. Telling the computer how long to collect data for and which sensors to use is
   (**the same as** / **different from**) when you're collecting data normally.

3. When you want to start collecting data, you have to (**press a button** / **shout 'Go'**).

4. All the measurements are stored in the (**sensor unit** / **back of the van**).

③ I took my temperature sensor on holiday.

The results I collected are shown on the graph below.

Write the correct letter from the graph next to each of the places I visited on my holiday.

Norwich ☐   Centre of the Sun ☐

Sweden ☐   South Pole ☐

Sahara Desert ☐

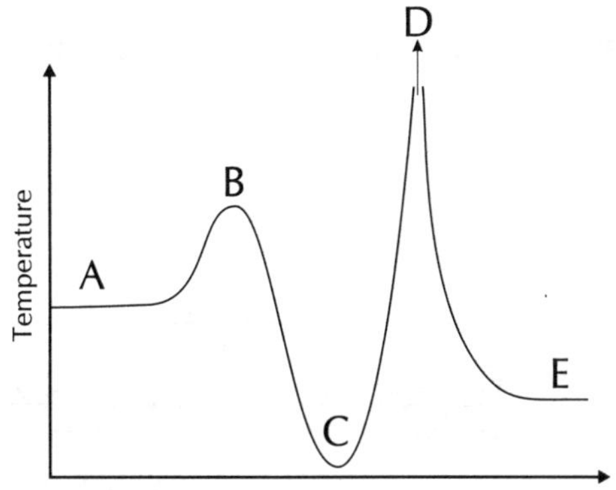

④ Write 'T' for True and 'F' for False.

1. When you get back you have to transfer your results onto a computer. ☐

2. Transferring results is called 'downplaying'. ☐

3. You have to click on the button marked 'cup of tea and a sticky bun, please'. ☐

4. The computer plots the results on a graph automatically. ☐

Interpreting Results

The software does most things for you — it measures the temperature or sound levels, draws the graphs and so on. But <u>you</u> have to work out what's happening in the graphs.

Work Out What's Going on in the Graphs

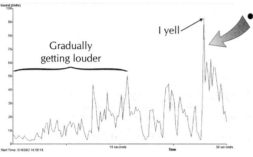

- This graph shows the noise level in my kitchen.

  - It starts off quiet — but gets gradually louder as more people come into the room and start talking.

    - There's a big peak near the end. That's when I dropped a hammer on my foot and yelled.

- This graph shows what happened when I put a temperature sensor in different places.

  - See how it takes a while for the readings to 'settle down' in each new place.

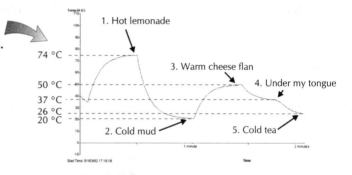

The First Record May Not be Accurate

In the temperature graph above, the readings took a while to settle at each new temperature.

✸ This means the first reading from a temperature sensor may not tell you how hot something is.

✸ You have to wait until the readings settle down.

Save your Graphs, or Paste Them Somewhere

You might need to save your graphs — or paste them into a word processor. It's easy.

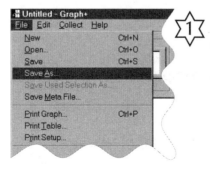

☆1 Use the 'File' menu to save your graph...

☆2 ...and the 'Edit' menu to 'Copy' it.

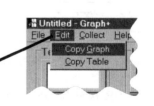

☆3 Once you've copied a graph, you can paste it into a word processor like any other picture.

Interpreting Results

① Mr. McAngry likes to shout at noisy classes.

This graph shows the noise level in Mr. McAngry's classroom during a 45-minute lesson.

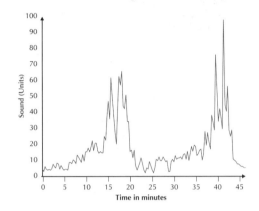

NO ONE TALKS EXCEPT ME!!!

1. Describe what happened to the noise levels between 0 and 13 minutes.

   ....

2. What happened to the noise levels between 15 and 20 minutes?

   ....

   What do you think may have caused this?

   ....

3. What happens to the noise levels for the rest of the lesson?
   What do you think might be happening?

   ....

   ....

USE A LIGHT SENSOR TO MONITOR THE LIGHT IN YOUR CLASSROOM FOR 24 HOURS

Connect a **light sensor** to the computer. Set up your monitoring program to **collect data** from the light sensor for 24 hours. Print out a **graph** of your results. How did the light change over the 24 hours? When were the lightest and darkest times over the 24 hours? Were there any big jumps in the data? What do you think caused these?

 **Computer Activity** _Keep Your Cool_

You'll need monitoring software and one or two temperature sensors for this project.

In this project you will:

See what affects how quickly water cools.

✓ Record the temperature of a cup of warm or hot water as it cools down.

✓ Change the conditions in some way, and do the same thing again.

✓ Try to find what has the biggest effect on the rate at which hot water cools.

What you need to do

1. Find the temperature of the room using your temperature sensor or a thermometer.

2. Get a cup and put some hot water in it.

3. Put a temperature sensor into the water.
   When the temperature reading settles down and stops going higher, write down the starting temperature of the water.

4. Record the temperature of the water for 20 minutes as it cools down.
   Use your monitoring software to draw a graph of your results.

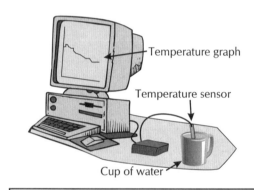
Temperature graph

Temperature sensor

Cup of water

BE VERY CAREFUL WITH HOT WATER.

Collect your results

 The aim of the project is to see how various things affect how quickly the water cools down.

 This means that you have to do the same thing a number of times — but each time, you do <u>one thing</u> different.

 Here are a few suggestions of things you could change:

- _Use cooler or hotter water — see if that cools more quickly or slowly._
- _Insulate one of the cups by wrapping thick material around it and covering it with a piece of cardboard. (You'll need to make a hole in the cardboard to put the temperature sensor through.)_
- _Add an ice cube to one of the cups of water._
- _Use a bigger or a smaller cup._
- _Use a different coloured cup. Or a cup made of a different material._